Photoelectron Spectroscopy and Molecular Orbital Theory

R E Ballard

BSc, PhD

School of Chemical Sciences
University of East Anglia

A HALSTED PRESS BOOK

John Wiley & Sons, New York

PHYSICS

Copyright © 1978 R E Ballard

British Library Cataloguing in Publication Data

Ballard R E
Photoelectron spectroscopy and molecular orbital theory
1. Photoelectron spectroscopy   2. Molecular orbitals
I. Title
535'.844   QC454.P48   78-40817

ISBN 0-85274-341-6 (Adam Hilger)
ISBN 0-470-26542-6 (Halsted Press)

Published in the USA by Halsted Press
a division of John Wiley & Sons, Inc., New York

Printed in Great Britain by J W Arrowsmith Ltd, Bristol BS3 2NT

Preface

The photoelectron spectrometer was described in 1914 by H Robinson and W F Rawlinson, but it was not until half a century later that it made its mark in chemistry. That there should have been such a long delay is remarkable, considering that the period in question was one in which great advances were being made in spectroscopy. The recent developments on the ultraviolet side of the technique can be traced back to A Terenin (1964) who employed ionising radiation from a hydrogen lamp. Such radiation has a useful energy of only 10·20 eV, and it was D W Turner's introduction of the helium lamp, with 21·21 eV, that first demonstrated the great power of the method. The modern technique can be said to date from Turner's innovation. The x-ray branch of the subject was developed by the Swedish school of K Siegbahn in the 1960s.

The first impressions created by the emergence of photoelectron spectroscopy were summed up by the late Professor C A Coulson in 1970: 'the single result of most significance is the complete vindication of the molecular orbital description of a molecule'. If the technique had not been forgotten in 1914, it might have played a great part in the development of molecular orbital theory but now, coming late in the day, its role is confirmatory. Two things can be said here: firstly, that the method will undoubtedly play a part in future developments and, secondly, that it provides an unequalled introduction to the theory for the student.

The next most important result, according to Coulson, was 'the confirmation of atomic changes within a molecule, as revealed by the chemical shift of an inner-shell ionisation potential of an atom when the environment of that atom is changed'. One consequence of this has been a fresh appreciation of L Pauling's ideas concerning electronegativity and ionicity. This part of the subject depends upon the use of x-radiation and is hardly touched upon, not because it is unimportant, but in order to assure the unity of the volume and to restrict its size as far as possible.

The subject matter has been used in my own lectures to undergraduates and MSc students for a number of years, and the aim of this book has been to substantiate the contention that photoelectron spectroscopy provides excellent introductory material for teaching the theory of molecular structure. In the few years that photoelectron spectroscopy has been with us, a large amount of data has already accumulated, and its assimilation into the curriculum is an important and an urgent task.

The first chapter will be about 50% revisory for those with a knowledge of traditional molecular and atomic spectroscopy; it is also intended to relate the subject to others, and to provide as consistent a framework and nomenclature as possible for the remainder of the book. The ability to relate molecules to others is one which every aspiring chemist should develop, and a complex web of such relationships can be revealed by photoelectron spectroscopy. Such connections sometimes involve molecules that the more traditional methods would not have brought together, such as B_2H_6, C_2H_2 and N_2, and also XeF_2 and CO_2. These relationships are implicit in the molecular orbitals themselves, of course, but photoelectron spectroscopy is required to bring them out; many more than are given here remain to be exploited by the student.

One day, no doubt, very accurate calculations will provide all the insight that a chemist needs to understand both the spectra and the chemistry of a molecule. For the time being, however, the best understanding is often achieved with the help of the simplest methods, and 'back-of-the-envelope' calculations are used unashamedly wherever possible. Nevertheless, there is a danger that such methods lead to over-simplified and erroneous conclusions unless they are confirmed by the more elaborate calculations obtained with the computer. Wherever possible, therefore, machine-computed results are quoted. Extensive use is also made of the beautiful computer-generated drawings of Jorgensen and Salem (1973) which show clearly the electronic density contours of molecular orbitals.

At the moment, it seems probable that photoelectron spectroscopy will, in the future, contribute mostly to surface chemistry and to the study of transient species. In these fields, certainly, it cannot be said that the technique has arrived too late.

I would like to thank Mr Hans Lempka of Helectros Developments and Dr A W Potts of King's College, London, for the use of their He(I) photoelectron spectrometers.

Ad majoram Dei gloriam

R E Ballard

School of Chemical Sciences
University of East Anglia

Contents

Contents

1 Preliminary Survey

1 The Interaction Between Light and Matter

There are many ways in which electromagnetic radiation can interact with matter. The study of these interactions constitutes several important subjects, including x-ray diffraction, the various kinds of spectroscopy, photochemistry, and so on. Much of our knowledge of the structure of matter derives from these fields of study.

In photoelectron spectroscopy the interaction known as the *photoelectric effect* is of primary importance; it results in the emission of an electron from that extranuclear cloud of core and valence electrons which is responsible for keeping atoms together as molecules. The photoelectron (e^-) possesses kinetic energy, the magnitude of which is dependent upon both the photon of light ($h\nu$) and the energy possessed in the extranuclear cloud. The measurement of this kinetic energy is a necessary part of photoelectron spectroscopy.

The simple absorption of a photon by matter, denoted M (representing an atom or molecule), can be expressed by

$$M + h\nu = M^* \tag{1.1}$$

where M^* is an excited state of M which is higher in energy by the quantity $h\nu$, and h is Planck's constant (see Appendix I).

In the excited state the excess energy implies metastability and a variety of different processes are known by which the energy is lost; among them are luminescence, dissociation, tautomerism, degradation to vibrational energy, and electron emission. The last is called alternatively *autoionisation* or *preionisation* and can be written

$$M^* = M^+ + e^-. \tag{1.2}$$

Clearly, autoionisation is a two-step process consisting of equation (1.1) followed by (1.2). Indeed, there may be more than two steps involved since M^* might undergo some other process before undergoing (1.2). Hence the kinetic energy of the photoelectron resulting from autoionisation depends upon the nature of the excited state, M^*.

The photoelectric effect, on the other hand, is a one-step process

$$M + h\nu = M^+ + e^- \tag{1.3}$$

and the kinetic energy is dependent on no intermediates. The time taken to complete the photoelectric effect cannot be less than the transit time of the photon across a molecule (about 10^{-15} s), but the time taken to complete autoionisation is longer, the slow step often being the loss of the electron (equation (1.2)).

In order for the absorption process (equation (1.1)) to take place there must be a match between the energy of the photon and the energy of the excited state. When this is so, the probability of simple absorption greatly outweighs the probability that the photoelectric effect will take place even when the photon possesses enough energy to cause ionisation. It is therefore necessary to avoid those photon energies having the same energy as excited states, and in practice this means using light of energy greater than 10–15 eV.

2   The Photoelectric Effect

The magnitude of the energy of a photon is $h\nu$, where ν is the frequency. The relationship between the wavelength, λ, and the velocity, c, is

$$\lambda \nu = c.$$

Although they have no rest mass, photons possess a momentum given by

$$mc = h\nu/c$$

as implied by the Einstein relation

$$\text{energy}, E = mc^2.$$

When a photon is absorbed its momentum and energy are both conserved, but since the momentum is smaller by a factor $1/c$ it can be neglected for our purposes.

The photoelectric effect produces an ion, M^+ (if the atom or molecule has zero charge), which is capable of existing in a number of different levels of electronic, vibrational, rotational and translational energy. The electronic states can be numbered M_0^+, M_1^+, M_3^+, etc, where M_0^+ represents the ion in its lowest-energy state. M_1^+ represents the first excited state, and so on. The energy of the nth electronic state can be denoted $E(M_n^+)$ for the ion and $E(M_n)$ for the molecule. The equation expressing energy conservation is

$$h\nu + E(M_0) = E(e^-) + E(M_n^+)$$

assuming that the molecule is in the ground state when the photon is absorbed. The energy of the electron is evidently

$$E(e^-) = h\nu + E(M_0) - E(M_n^+).$$

The difference in energy, $E(M_n^+) - E(M_0)$, is called the nth *ionisation energy* of M, which is a positive quantity as long as M is stable.

In photoelectron spectroscopy the frequency of the photon is kept constant and the number of electrons emitted per constant time interval is measured for all values of the kinetic energy between $h\nu$ and zero. A plot of electron current so measured against ionisation energy reveals the values of the ionisation energies of the substance being examined; the current is zero where $h\nu - E(e^-)$ corresponds to no ionisation energy and has maxima where correspondence does occur.

The energy of the electron can be considered for our purposes to be purely kinetic, but the kinetic energy of the ion is usually negligible as the following argument makes clear. As the ion and electron separate, they move apart with equal and opposite momenta,

$$mu = MU$$ (2.1)

where m is the mass of the electron, u is its velocity, etc. The relative velocity, V, is independent of the centre of mass (which moves so as to conserve the momentum of the photon),

$$V = u + U.$$

From equation (2.1),

$$V = U(1 + M/m)$$
$$= u(1 + m/M).$$

The kinetic energies are

$$\tfrac{1}{2}MU^2 = \frac{1}{2M}\left\{\frac{mMV}{m+M}\right\}^2$$

$$\tfrac{1}{2}mu^2 = \frac{1}{2m}\left\{\frac{mMV}{m+M}\right\}^2.$$

The relative kinetic energies of the separating products are inversely proportional to their masses. The lightest nucleus is about 1836 times as heavy as the electron and therefore the kinetic energy of the ion is usually several thousand times less than that of the photoelectron.

The photoelectron spectrum of H_2 is exceptional in that the rotational structure has been resolved (Åsbrink 1970a, b, Peatman 1976), but it was found necessary to correct for the kinetic energy of H_2^+, which is equal to 0·00027 times the energy of the photoelectron. The magnitudes of the various quanta appearing in the photoelectron spectrum of H_2 are as follows. The smallest rotational quantum† (of H_2^+) = 0·0074 eV; the vibrational quantum (of H_2^+) = 0·288 eV, and the lowest ionisation energy (of H_2) = 15·42 eV.

3 Photoelectron Spectroscopy

A photoelectron spectrometer is really a very simple instrument consisting in no more than a source of monochromatic radiation, a sample compartment where the photoelectric effect takes place, an energy analyser which can be controlled to allow only electrons of specific energy to pass, and an electron detector. Electrons are a reactive species having only a small penetrating power for matter, so that it is necessary to reduce the pressure along their path. No branch of spectroscopy can boast of a wider variety of types of energy analyser than photoelectron spectroscopy, but a discussion of these is beyond the scope of this book (see, for example, Klemperer 1971). The photocurrent measured by the detector is sent to some recording device such as a chart recorder or a multichannel analyser, and is plotted against the setting of the energy analyser to provide the spectrum.

---

† The rotational energy is given by $BJ(J+1)$, where J is the rotational quantum number and B = 0·0037 eV in the case of H_2^+. Thus for the transition between states of rotational values $J = 0$ and $J = 1$, the energy is $2BJ$. Vibrational energy is discussed in subsequent chapters.

The absorption of light along a path of length d of the sample is governed by the equation

$$F/F_0 = \exp(-n\sigma d), \tag{3.1}$$

where F_0 is the incident and F is the emergent light intensity (photons area^{-1} time^{-1}), n is the number of atoms (or molecules) per unit volume, and σ is the absorption cross section. The cross section has the dimensions of area and is the effective area presented to the light beam by the atom or molecule. Values of σ range from zero up to several Å^2 for atoms, the latter values being of the same order of magnitude as the 'real area' calculated from the atomic radii derived from atomic separation distances in molecules.

The difference in light intensity as the beam passes through the sample is given by

$$F_0 - F = F_0(1 - 1 + n\sigma d - \ldots)$$

$$\approx F_0 n\sigma d.$$

The above approximation neglects terms above first order in $n\sigma d$, and it is valid as long as $n\sigma d$ is small, a condition which is easily attained in the gas phase. The quantum yield, Q, is the probability that the absorption of light will produce a photoelectron. Ideally, $Q = 1$ and it begins to approach this value in most cases when the light energy exceeds 10 eV. The photoelectron current is given by

$$i = QF_0 n\sigma d.$$

The photocurrent varies with the energy of the photoelectron and this can be made explicit by writing i as a function of this energy, $i(E)$. In practice, a photoelectron spectrometer measures $i(E)$ within a range of energies, $E \pm \Delta E$, where $2\Delta E$ is the range of electron energies passed by the analyser. The value of $i(E)$ usually depends upon ΔE as well as upon E, and if two ionisation energies lie closer together than ΔE it is not possible to distinguish them clearly. It is therefore desirable to keep ΔE as low as possible. In most instruments it is found that $\Delta E \propto E^{1/2}$ and therefore the use of light of low energy enhances the resolution (compare, for example, the spectrum of Ne in figures 3.1 and 17.2). On the other hand, it is necessary to employ high-energy light in order to avoid autoionisation and also to study the higher ionisation energies. The most desirable procedure is to measure each photoelectron spectrum with a range of light energies. A further practical point is that the energy of the electrons passed by the analyser varies with the gas pressure in some cases, and is also affected by other adventitious variables such as the development of static charge on interior surfaces. It is therefore necessary to standardise each spectrum by running a substance of known ionisation energy with the sample.

Photoelectron spectroscopy naturally falls into two classes: high-energy or x-ray, and low-energy or UV photoelectron spectroscopy. The former employs photon energies of higher than 1000 eV and is sometimes called ESCA (electron spectroscopy for chemical analysis), and the latter frequently uses He(I) radiation of 21·21 eV or He(II) radiation of 40·77 eV. These designations refer to the He transition, $1s2p(^1P_0) \rightarrow 1s^2(^1S)$, and the He$^-$ transition, $2p(^2P_0) \rightarrow 1s(^2S)$, respectively, which produce a high intensity at the energies mentioned.

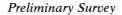

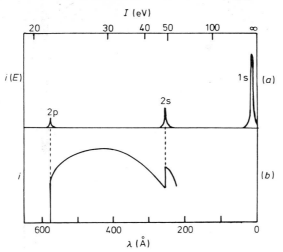

Figure 3.1. (*a*) The photoelectron spectrum of neon obtained using x-radiation of energy 1253·6 eV (Siegbahn *et al* 1969). (*b*) The photoionisation spectrum of neon (Weisler 1956). Peaks in spectrum (*a*) correspond to edges in spectrum (*b*).

An *ionisation spectrum* can be defined as a plot of the total photocurrent, *i*, against *hν*. In figure 3.1 the ionisation spectrum and the photoelectron spectrum of neon are given. One of the advantages of the photoelectron spectrum over the ionisation spectrum can be seen in this figure; the ionisation spectrum shows two edges, whereas in the photoelectron spectrum there are peaks. The three peaks in the photoelectron spectrum are due to the processes

$$h\nu + \text{Ne}(1s^2 2s^2 2p^6) \rightarrow \text{Ne}^+(1s^2 2s^2 2p^5) + e^-$$

$$h\nu + \text{Ne}(1s^2 2s^2 2p^6) \rightarrow \text{Ne}^+(1s^2 2s^1 2p^6) + e^-$$

$$h\nu + \text{Ne}(1s^2 2s^2 2p^6) \rightarrow \text{Ne}^+(1s^1 2s^2 2p^6) + e^-.$$

In the first process a 2p orbital is ionised; in the second a 2s orbital, and in the third a 1s orbital. They give an obvious and well resolved structure in the photoelectron spectrum, but not in the ionisation spectrum. Spectrum (*a*) is given approximately by differentiating spectrum (*b*).

Another more practical matter is that for the measurement of ionisation spectra, a whole range of wavelengths of light is required rather than just one. Only with the aid of the synchrotron, which is a large and costly installation, could the ionisation spectrum of neon be obtained in the 1s region. On the other hand, monochromatic light is cheaply available from the resonance lines of the noble gases and the x-ray lines of the elements provide monochromatic x-radiation.

4 Rydberg Series

The term 'line spectrum' arises from the early method of photographically recording the optical spectra of atoms, which was achieved by exciting the atoms in a flame, an electric arc or an electric spark, and passing the light through a spectrometer in such a way that a particular frequency formed a line on a photographic plate. Atoms were found to give a series of narrow lines and molecules gave broader images called 'bands'. The reason for the broadening of molecular spectra was the presence of vibrational and rotational energies which caused the presence of numerous overlapping lines.

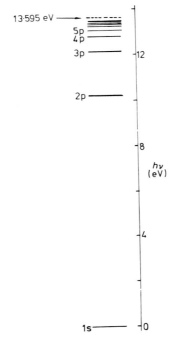

Figure 4.1. The Lyman series of atomic hydrogen. The energy of separation of the Rydberg terms gradually diminishes until at 13·595 eV the spectrum becomes continuous.

In figure 4.1 the frequencies of a series of lines observed in the spectrum of atomic hydrogen are plotted. This set, called the Lyman series after the name of its discoverer, is due to transitions of the electron between the 1s orbital and 2p, 3p, 4p, etc,

$$h\nu + H(1s^1) \rightarrow H(np^1).$$

The energies of the lines are given by

$$h\nu = R(1 - 1/n^2) \tag{4.1}$$

where the Rydberg constant, R, has the value 13·595 eV, and the *principal quantum number*, n, which must be an integer, denotes the excited level, np. The Lyman series extends from 10·19 to 13·595 eV, where the lines become so close that no separation can be seen and the series has become a 'continuum'. In the continuum region ionisation occurs,

$$hv + H(1s^1) \rightarrow H^+ + e^-$$

and the onset of the continuum at $13 \cdot 595$ eV is the ionisation energy of the 1s orbital of hydrogen. Many ionisation energies have been accurately measured by finding such ionisation limits, but if a sufficient number of terms can be found to establish an equation such as (4.1) the ionisation energy can be calculated by putting $n = \infty$.

Other series for hydrogen can be expressed by the equation

$$hv = R(1/n_2^2 - 1/n_1^2) \qquad (4.2)$$

and are called the Balmer $(n_2 = 2)$, Paschen $(n_2 = 3)$, Brackett $(n_2 = 4)$ and Pfund $(n_2 = 5)$ series. The Balmer series is due to the transitions

$$H(2p) \rightarrow H(ns)$$

$$H(2p) \rightarrow H(nd)$$

$$H(2s) \rightarrow H(np).$$

Only in one-electron systems such as H, He^+, Li^{2+}, etc, are these transitions of the same energy, otherwise electron–electron repulsion raises the degeneracy (see p 19).

In polyelectronic atoms, equation (4.2) can still be used but the values of n are no longer integral. An effective quantum number, $n - \delta$, is involved,

$$hv = R\left\{ \text{constant} - \frac{1}{(n - \delta)^2} \right\}, \qquad (4.3)$$

and δ is called the *quantum defect*. Here, n is integral but the quantum defect is not. Equation (4.3) applies to molecules as well as polyelectronic atoms. Much of the data from the study of Rydberg series have been collected by Moore (1952) and Herzberg (1950).

Only in a few molecules can Rydberg series be discovered, for there are difficulties in picking them out and, in addition to ionisation continua, there are also dissociation and other continua. However, in some molecules Rydberg series can be found in which the first few members are broad but the later ones become progressively more sharp and more like atomic lines until an ionisation continuum is reached. For example, in figure 4.2 the absorption spectrum of methyl iodide exhibits two Rydberg series with ionisation limits of $9 \cdot 49$ and $10 \cdot 11$ eV. These ionisation energies are also clearly seen in the photoelectron spectrum in figure 4.3, together with several others which are not detectable in the absorption spectrum.

The gradual change from bands to lines along the series is due to the increasing size of the electronic orbital of the excited electron in the Rydberg state of the molecule. Very roughly, the radius of the electronic orbital of an atom increases as n^2, where n is the principal quantum number. When the radius is very large the orbital of the excited electron of a polyelectronic atom or molecules is quasi-hydrogenic since there is effectively a unit positive charge at the centre, and the other electrons are too far away to interact significantly. Hence, if the ground-state configuration is M and the ion is M^+, Rydberg states of a molecule could be written

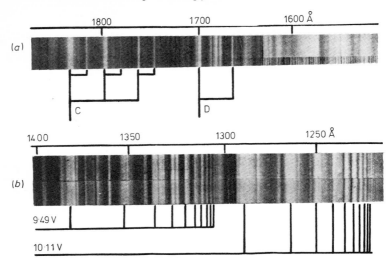

Figure 4.2. The absorption spectrum of methyl iodide taken on a photographic plate. In (*a*) the region from 1550 to 1850 Å is covered and in (*b*) the region from 1220 to 1400 Å. The two Rydberg series with limits at 9·49 and 10·11 eV are due to the transitions of a molecular orbital largely consisting of the 'lone-pair' atomic orbitals of iodine. In atomic iodine itself, the lowest ionisation energy of these 5p orbitals occurs at 10·45 eV and the spin–orbit splitting of the $^2P_{1/2}$ and the $^2P_{3/2}$ states is 0·94 eV. Note the progressive sharpening of the bands as the energy approaches the series limit. The series labelled C and D are of uncertain origin. Photograph kindly supplied by Professor W C Price.

$M^+(np^1)$, in analogy with the Lyman states of hydrogen. That the molecular core, M^+, is in a quasi-ionised state is evidenced by the close resemblance found between the vibrational progressions of Rydberg spectra and photoelectron spectra. In cyclopropane, for example, the energy of the vibrational progression is 0·0607 eV (490 cm^{-1}) in both types of spectra, whereas in the molecular ground state the nearest is 0·0918 eV (741 cm^{-1}), as observed in the IR spectrum (Basch *et al* 1969).

The presence of a heavy atom in the molecule often leads to the splitting of bands by spin–orbit interaction, and the splittings observed in the Rydberg series are characteristic of the ionised (rather than neutral) molecule. One example which has been mentioned, methyl iodide, evidently has a pair of Rydberg series split by spin–orbit interaction. Another case is CSe_2, where the splitting is 0·26 eV, and the

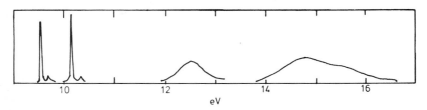

Figure 4.3. The photoelectron spectrum of methyl iodide (Potts *et al* 1970). The sharp peaks with maxima at 9·54 and 10·16 eV correspond with the series limits of figure 4.2.

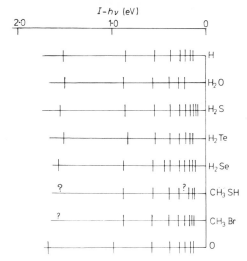

Figure 4.4. Term values for the Rydberg series of a number of molecules and for the Lyman series of hydrogen. Missing terms are denoted by a question mark.

same separation is found in the photoelectron spectrum (Cradock *et al* 1975).

The energy difference, $I - h\nu$, is called the *term value* (Mulliken 1976). The closer a Rydberg orbital of a molecule is in kind to the corresponding orbital of hydrogen in the Lyman series, the closer will be their term values. Some term values are plotted in figure 4.4, together with the values for the Lyman series showing how the energies of molecular Rydberg states match hydrogenic ones. It is possible to see in some cases where terms in the molecular spectra have been missed.

5 Angular Momentum

Niels Bohr's assumption that the angular momentum of an electron in an atomic orbit,

$$M = nh/(2\pi),$$

where n is integral, is logically connected to de Broglie's hypothesis that there is a wave motion associated with the electron of wavelength h/p, where p is the linear momentum of the electron. If the wave is continuous about the atom and the orbit has a radius R, then $2\pi R = n\lambda = nh/p$ and Bohr's assumption follows since $M = pR$. These considerations were prompted by the study of the optical spectra of atoms.

However, wave motion is characterised by a wave equation, generally called the wavefunction in quantum mechanics, and denoted by ϕ or ψ (Appendix II). These characterise orbitals and are functions of space (x, y, z) and time (t). The usefulness of the wavefunction derives from the possibility of calculating the properties of the electron in the orbital. Such calculations are made with the help of operators (denoted by ^); for example, the operator for linear momentum in the x direction is

$$\hat{p}_x = \frac{-ih}{2\pi} \frac{d}{dx} \qquad (5.1)$$

where $i = (-1)^{1/2}$.

The wavefunction is said to be an *eigenfunction* (exact or characteristic function) of the operator having *eigenvalues* (exact or characteristic values) of the operator,

(operator) . (eigenfunction) = (eigenvalue) . (eigenfunction).

For example,

$$\hat{p}_x(\phi) = p_x(\phi).$$

Another property of the electronic eigenfunction of an electron is that its square, evaluated at any position in space, is proportional to the electronic density, q, at that position. Since eigenfunctions are sometimes complex quantities (that is, containing i), this is expressed by

$$q(x, y, z) = N^2 \iiint \phi\phi^* \, dx \, dy \, dz$$

where ϕ^* is the complex conjugate of ϕ. For brevity, the above equation can be written

$$q(x, y, z) = N^2 \int \phi^2 \, dV$$

where dV is an infinitesimal volume around the point (x, y, z).

The *normalisation constant, N,* can be evaluated from the requirement that the electronic density integrated over all space for any one-electron function must be unity,

$$N^2 \int_0^\infty \phi^2 \, dV = 1.$$

Wavefunctions fulfilling the condition

$$\int_0^\infty \phi^2 \, dV = 1$$

are said to be *normalised*.

Supposing that the electron occupies some normalised orbital, ϕ, its momentum along the x direction is

$$\mathbf{p}_x = \int_0^\infty \phi\hat{p}_x\phi^* \, dV. \qquad (5.2)$$

The bold characters $\mathbf{p}_x$ and $\hat{\mathbf{p}}_x$ are used to emphasise that momentum is a vector quantity wherever this emphasis is required. A shortened form of equation (5.2) is

$$\mathbf{p}_x = \langle\phi|\hat{\mathbf{p}}_x|\phi\rangle.$$

In equation (5.1) it is seen that the momentum operator is imaginary and therefore if the wavefunction is real, the value of p_x given by equation (5.2) is also imaginary. Only real quantities are observable in quantum mechanics, and therefore real wavefunctions possess zero momentum. This remark applies equally to angular momentum, which is related to linear momentum by

$$M = r \times p \tag{5.3}$$

where r is the radius vector from the axis of rotation to the electron ($\times$ represents the vector product and, by the rules for vector multiplication, the angular momentum is directed perpendicularly to the plane of rotation). Taking the direction of the angular momentum to be z it is often convenient to write

$$M_z = xp_y - yp_x. \tag{5.4}$$

By equations similar to (5.1) the operator for angular momentum about the z axis is

$$\hat{M}_z = \frac{-ih}{2\pi}(x \, \mathrm{d/dy} - y \, \mathrm{d/dx})$$

$$= \frac{-ih}{2\pi} \mathrm{d/d}\phi \tag{5.5}$$

where ϕ is the angle given in figure 5.1.

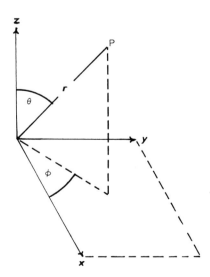

Figure 5.1. The point P is defined either by (x, y, z) or by (r, θ, ϕ), the latter being the spherical coordinates. A plane is defined by two lines, the perpendicular from the point to the (x, y) plane and the line joining the point to the origin; ϕ is the angle between this plane and the (x, z) plane. The angle between the z axis and the line joining the point to the origin is θ. $x = r \sin \theta \cos \phi$; $y = r \sin \theta \sin \phi$; $z = r \cos \theta$.

We have already seen that only complex functions possess angular momentum, and this statement can now be connected with degeneracy. If there are two real wavefunctions of the same symmetry species and energy, they are said to be *degenerate*. Suppose that ϕ_1 and ϕ_2 are such a pair. It is found that any linear combination of ϕ_1 and ϕ_2 makes an equally valid wavefunction; for example,

$$\Phi_1 = \phi_1 + c_1\phi_2$$

$$\Phi_2 = \phi_1 + c_2\phi_2$$

where c_1 and c_2 are constants. It is always possible and valid to make these constants imaginary, so that Φ_1 and Φ_2 are complex and give a real momentum when operated upon by $\hat{M}_z$.

It will be shown later that without the presence of angular momentum there can be no spin–orbit interaction. It is therefore concluded that only degenerate electronic orbitals undergo spin–orbit interaction.

6   Electronic Orbitals of Hydrogen

The operator for energy is called the Hamiltonian, after the 19th century mathematician, and it is denoted by H. The energy of the normalised wavefunction ϕ is

$$E(\phi) = \langle \phi | H | \phi \rangle. \tag{6.1}$$

The well known eigenfunctions for the hydrogen atom (Pauling and Wilson 1935) derive from the operator

$$H = \frac{1}{2m}p^2 - \frac{e^2}{r} \tag{6.2}$$

where m is the electronic mass and hence the first term represents the kinetic energy. The second term is the Coulombic attraction between the nucleus and the electron, where r is the separation between them.

The hydrogenic functions can be written

$$\phi(n, l, m) = R(r)\Theta(\theta)\exp(im\phi) \tag{6.3}$$

where n is the *principal quantum number* appearing in equation (4.1), l is the *azimuthal quantum number*, and m is the *magnetic quantum number*.

The principal quantum number is related to the energy through

$$\langle \phi | H | \phi \rangle = -R/n^2 \tag{6.4}$$

where R is the Rydberg constant. From equation (6.4) the expressions for the Rydberg series of hydrogen (§ 4) are derived.

The azimuthal quantum number is related to the orbital angular momentum through

$$\langle \phi | \hat{M}^2 | \phi \rangle = l(l+1)h^2/(2\pi)^2 \tag{6.5}$$

and the operator for total angular momentum is

$$\hat{\boldsymbol{M}}^2 = \hat{\boldsymbol{M}}_x^2 + \hat{\boldsymbol{M}}_y^2 + \hat{\boldsymbol{M}}_z^2.$$

The reason for using $\hat{\boldsymbol{M}}^2$ is connected with the uncertainty principle; it is impossible to know precisely all three of the magnitudes of $\boldsymbol{M}_x$, $\boldsymbol{M}_y$ and $\boldsymbol{M}_z$ (Kauzmann 1957). However it is possible to know $\boldsymbol{M}^2$ and one of the components, the magnetic quantum number being related to the component through, for example,

$$\langle\phi|\hat{\boldsymbol{M}}_z|\phi\rangle = mh/(2\pi). \tag{6.6}$$

The magnetic quantum number is so named because in a magnetic field there is a difference in energy between orbitals having different magnetic quantum numbers. This energy difference arises because the magnetic quantum number indicates the magnitude of the orbital momentum component along one one direction, say z, as in equation (6.6), that is, it indicates the orientation of the momentum. In a uniform magnetic field the interaction energy with the orbital moment depends upon the orientation (the *Zeeman effect*).

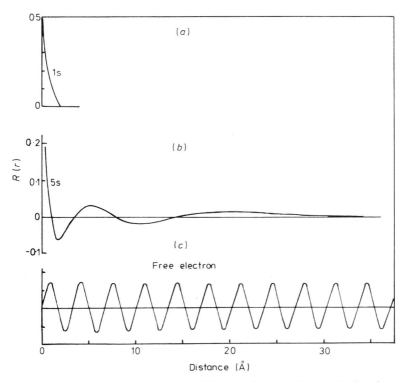

Figure 6.1. (*a*) and (*b*) The radial part, $R(r)$, of the hydrogenic 1s and 5s functions plotted against the distance from the nucleus, *r*. (*c*) The plot for the free electron of kinetic energy of about 13 eV on the same scale, but at a distance far from the nucleus. Close to the nucleus there is a distortion of the free-electron function by the nuclear field.

Allowed values of the quantum numbers are

$$n = 1, 2, 3, \ldots$$

$$l = 0, 1, 2, 3, \ldots (n-1)$$

$$m = -l, (-l+1), (-l+2), \ldots -1, 0, 1, \ldots (l-2), (l-1), l.$$

Thus for $n = 2$ allowed values are $l = 0$ and $l = 1$; $m = 0$ and $m = -1, 0, 1$. We see that the number of different values of m is $(2l+1)$.

The quantum numbers n and l are also often used for the classification of atomic orbitals other than those of hydrogen. For l, instead of the numbers 0, 1, 2, 3, $\ldots$, the letters s, p, d, f, $\ldots$ are employed. Thus a 4f orbital has $n = 4$ and $l = 3$.

The functions $R(r)$ and $\Theta(\theta)$ are given by Pauling and Wilson (1935). The radial function, $R(r)$, controls the size of the orbital; plots of $R(r)$ are given in figure 6.1 for the 1s and 5s orbitals of hydrogen. It is noteworthy that the 5s orbital is much larger than the 1s orbital (as discussed in § 4) and that there are *nodal surfaces* where the wave equation is zero at certain values of r.

The functions $\Theta(\theta) \exp(im\phi)$ are called spherical harmonics and their symmetry properties are important in what follows in this book. From them comes the concept of the 'shapes' of the electronic orbitals of atoms, which are given in table 6.1.

Table 6.1. Spherical harmonics.

	Polar coordinates	Cartesian coordinates
s	1	1
p_z	$\cos\theta$	z/r
p_x	$\sin\theta\cos\phi$	x/r
p_y	$\sin\theta\sin\phi$	y/r
d_{z^2}	$3\cos^2\theta - 1$	$(3z^2 - r^2)/r^2$
d_{yz}	$\sin\theta\cos\theta\sin\phi$	yz/r^2
d_{xz}	$\sin\theta\cos\theta\cos\phi$	xz/r^2
d_{xy}	$\sin^2\theta\sin 2\phi$	xy/r^2
$d_{x^2-y^2}$	$\sin^2\theta\cos 2\phi$	$(x^2 - y^2)/r^2$
f_{z^3}	$5\cos^3\theta - 3\cos\theta$	$(5z^3 - 3r^2z)/r^3$
f_{yz^2}	$\sin\theta(5\cos^2\theta - 1)\sin\phi$	$y(5z^2 - r^2)/r^3$
f_{xz^2}	$\sin\theta(5\cos^2\theta - 1)\cos\phi$	$x(5z^2 - r^2)/r^3$
f_{xyz}	$\sin^2\theta\cos\theta\sin 2\phi$	xyz/r^3
$f_{z(x^2-y^2)}$	$\sin^2\theta\cos\theta\cos 2\phi$	$z(x^2 - y^2)/r^3$
f_{y^3}	$\sin^3\theta\sin 3\phi$	$y(y^2 - 3x^2)/r^3$
f_{x^3}	$\sin^3\theta\cos 3\phi$	$x(x^2 - 3y^2)/r^3$

7   Transition Probability

The wavefunction for the free electron of wavelength λ can be expressed by

$$\chi = \exp(i2\pi r/\lambda) \tag{7.1}$$

$$= \cos\theta + i\sin\theta$$

where θ is $2\pi r/\lambda$.

During the photoelectric effect the photoelectron passes to χ from the orbital ϕ_j of negative energy, in which it was bound to the nuclei of a molecule or the nucleus of an atom. At the same time the orbitals of M change or relax to the orbitals of M^+. Assuming that there are two electrons in every orbital the *configuration* of M is $\phi_1^2 \phi_2^2 \ldots \phi_j^2 \ldots$, and the configuration of M^+ is $\psi_1^2 \psi_2^2 \ldots \psi_j^1 \chi^1 \ldots$ The ϕ orbitals of M after the transition have become the ψ orbitals of M_j^+, the ion with an electron removed from the jth orbital.

The probability, p, that the transition takes place through the agency of the electric field of the light wave is given by the use of the operator, er, where e is the electronic charge and r is the electronic position vector with regard to some arbitrary fixed point or origin. This *transition dipole moment* operator is the largest of a series of terms that can be derived for the interaction of M with the photon; the others are insignificant below 200 eV (Mott and Sneddon 1948). The equation for p is

$$p \simeq (4\pi^2/h)(\phi_j|er|\chi)^2. \qquad (7.2)$$

In order to evaluate equation (7.2) it is necessary to know the form of χ over the range of distances at which the photoelectron finds itself at the moment of interaction with the photon (the average distance from the nucleus can be defined as the distance at which

$$\int 4\pi r^2 \phi_j^2 \, dr$$

reaches its maximum value). However, equation (7.1) is not correct at short

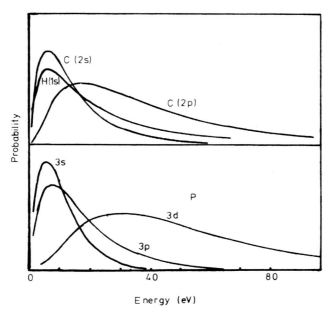

Figure 7.1. Plots of the ionisation probability (equations (7.1) and (7.2)) against the energy of the photoelectron for some orbitals of H, C and P (Schweig and Thiel 1974).

distances from nuclei because χ is then distorted by the nuclear field. Accurate calculations are available only for atoms and H_2^+.

Perhaps because of these theoretical difficulties there have been few attempts to measure the relative intensities of photoelectron spectra. All that is required experimentally is to take account of the variation in the efficiency of collection of photoelectrons as their kinetic energy varies, and to take precautions with the angle of collection (§ 44).

The transition dipole moment varies with the energy of the photoelectron (figure 7.1). This variation is readily understood when it is realised that the transition dipole moment is approximately proportional to the *overlap integral*, $\langle \phi_j | \chi \rangle$, which is dependent on the wavelength of χ. If the wavelength is so small that χ undergoes many changes of sign where ϕ_j changes slowly, then the overlap integral is also small. Consequently, maximal intensity occurs very approximately when $h\nu = 2I$, where I is the ionisation energy. Some calculations of p using the approximate form of χ given in equation (7.1) are plotted in figure 7.1. It is apparent from this figure, for example, that the use of 21·21 eV radiation gives roughly the same probability for ionisation of phosphorus 3d as for 3p orbitals, whereas 40·81 eV ionises 3p relatively poorly. It is clearly possible to learn something of the composition of molecular orbitals from a study of the variation in the photoelectron spectrum with $h\nu$, but few comprehensive attempts to do this have been made.

As a rule of thumb, the intensity of a photoelectron peak is proportional to the number of electrons occupying the orbital, but this is far from correct if the peaks being compared derive from orbitals of very different atomic composition.

8   Polyelectronic Atoms

It is assumed that the wavefunctions of polyelectronic atoms can be written as products of one-electron functions, ϕ; for example, in the same form as equation (6.3). The starting point of the discussion is therefore an approximate wavefunction of the form

$$\Psi = \phi_1(1)\phi_2(2)\phi_3(3)\ldots$$

$$= \prod_i \phi_i(\alpha). \tag{8.1}$$

The meaning of $\phi_i(\alpha)$ is that the electron labelled α is in the one-electron function labelled i.

The Hamiltonian of equation (6.2) now requires elaboration; the term for the Coulombic attraction of the electron and the nucleus is $-Ze^2/r$, where Z is the atomic number of the nucleus. For every electron present there will be a term such as equation (6.2) in the Hamiltonian, and the mathematical advantage of equation (8.1) is that it allows such a Hamiltonian to operate individually upon every ϕ without affecting the others. In mathematical language it allows the separation of the variables. Another justification for equation (8.1) is the experimental result that transitions of a single electron from one orbital to another do actually occur without the other electrons being much affected.

The solutions arrived at from this starting point share with the hydrogenic functions the property that they are degenerate where they differ only in l quantum number. This result is contrary to experiment and originates from the failure to include in the Hamiltonian terms for the electron–electron repulsions, e^2/r_{ij}, where r_{ij} is the separation distance between electrons i and j. The spin–orbit interaction discussed in § 36 is also omitted.

A shortcoming of equation (8.1) is the neglect of the principle that electrons cannot be definitely assigned to specific orbitals; electrons behave as though they are continuously exchanged between orbitals. Moreover, there is the requirement that electronic wavefunctions are *antisymmetric with respect to electron exchange*, that is, they change sign if an electron passes from one orbital to another. These points are dealt with by writing Ψ as a *Slater determinant*; for example,

$$\Psi = \frac{1}{\sqrt{2}} \begin{vmatrix} \phi_1(1) & \phi_2(1) \\ \phi_1(2) & \phi_2(2) \end{vmatrix}$$

$$= \frac{1}{\sqrt{2}} \{\phi_1(1)\phi_2(2) - \phi_1(2)\phi_2(1)\}. \tag{8.2}$$

The general expression for the Slater determinant is

$$\Psi = \frac{1}{\sqrt{n!}} \begin{vmatrix} \phi_1(1)\phi_2(1) & \cdots & \phi_n(1) \\ \phi_1(2)\phi_2(2) & \cdots & \phi_n(2) \\ \vdots & & \\ \phi_1(n)\phi_2(n) & \cdots & \phi_n(n) \end{vmatrix} \tag{8.3}$$

9 Electron Spin

The hypothesis of *electron spin* was put forward to explain certain degeneracies which seemed to require a quantum number in addition to those of § 6. Goudsmit and Uhlenbeck assumed that for a single electron there are two possible spin functions, α and β, whose spin quantum numbers have the values, $m_s = \pm\frac{1}{2}$. The spin quantum is analogous to m in equation (6.6) and there is a spin operator, $\hat{S}_z$, which is analogous to $\hat{M}_z$,

$$\langle \alpha | \hat{S}_z | \alpha \rangle = \tfrac{1}{2} h/(2\pi)$$
$$\langle \beta | \hat{S}_z | \beta \rangle = -\tfrac{1}{2} h/(2\pi). \tag{9.1}$$

The operator for total spin angular momentum is

$$\hat{S}^2 = \hat{S}_x^2 + \hat{S}_y^2 + \hat{S}_z^2$$

and for a single electron,

$$\langle \alpha | \hat{S}^2 | \alpha \rangle = \langle \beta | \hat{S}^2 | \beta \rangle$$
$$= \tfrac{1}{2}(\tfrac{1}{2} + 1)(h/2\pi)^2. \tag{9.2}$$

Equation (6.5) is analogous to the above, and the total spin quantum number, s, which takes the value $\frac{1}{2}$, is the analogue of l.

The origin of electronic spin can be found in the theory of relativity; the electron may be pictured as spinning about its own axis, but the fact that only two eigenstates are observed and that these involve half-integral quantum numbers suggests that any picture based solely upon classical or non-relativistic formulations is illusory.

The spin functions can be included in the one-electron functions of § 8 simply by multiplication, and ϕ becomes either $\phi\alpha$ or $\phi\beta$. This is so because the spin operators do not operate upon ϕ and the other operators do not operate on the spin functions. The operators are said to *commute*; for example,

$$H\hat{S}_z(\phi\alpha) = \hat{S}_z H(\phi\alpha).$$

When operators commute they both have exact eigenvalues for the same eigenfunctions; if they do not commute they cannot both have exact eigenvalues for the same eigenfunctions.

10   Atomic States

In general, an atom in a particular configuration can exist in a number of states. For example, a carbon atom in the $1s^2 2s^2 2p^2$ configuration has states labelled ^1S, ^1D and ^3P. It is possible for these to interact and mix with the states of other configurations, but this complication will be ignored for the time being.

The labels ^1S, etc, are derived from the quantum numbers l and s which are summed over all the electrons in the atom to give the resultants L and S. There are $(2L+1)$ different possible values of M_L for a given value of L, where M_L is the total magnetic quantum number. Similarly, there are $(2S+1)$ different values of M_S, which is the resultant obtained by adding all the m_s quantum numbers. In the labels the superscript gives the spin degeneracy; ^{2S+1}P becomes ^3P when $S = 1$. The letters S, P, D, . . . , denote that $L = 0, 1, 2, . . .$, respectively.

A shorthand notation for the one-electron state with $m = 2$ and $m_s = +\frac{1}{2}$ is 2^+; for $m = 3$ and $m_s = -\frac{1}{2}$ we can write 3^-, etc. The allowed states of a given configuration can be derived with the aid of a table such as 10.1, where the example is p^2.

Table 10.1 complies with the *Pauli Principle* that no electron can have the same set of quantum numbers as another. The use of such a table is straightforward, and

Table 10.1. One-electron functions for p^2; the *L–S* scheme.

	M_S		
M_L	1	0	-1
2		$(1^+, 1^-)$	
1	$(1^+, 0^+)$	$(1^+, 0^-), (1^-, 0^+)$	$(1^-, 0^-)$
0	$(1^+, -1^+)$	$(1^+, -1^-), (1^-, -1^+), (0^+, 0^-)$	$(1^-, -1^-)$
-1	$(-1^+, 0^+)$	$(-1^+, 0^-), (-1^-, 0^+)$	$(-1^-, 0^-)$
-2		$(-1^+, -1^-)$	

Table 10.2. Terms of equivalent electrons.

s^2	^1S
p, p^5	^2P
p^2, p^4	$^1(S, D), ^3P$
p^3	$^2(P, D), ^4S$
d, d^9	^2D
d^2, d^8	$^1(S, D, G), ^3(P, F)$
d^3, d^7	$^2(P, D, F, G, H), ^4(P, F)$
d^4, d^6	$^1(S, D, F, G, I), ^3(P, D, F, G, H), ^5D$
d^5	$^2(S, P, D, F, G, H, I), ^4(P, D, F, G), ^6S$

the existence of the maximum value, $M = 2$, implies that a D state is present. Since $M = 2$ arises from $(1^+, 1^-)$ it is clear that $M_s = 0$, that is, we have a singlet state, ^1D. Such a state has the following possible values of M_L; 2, 1, 0, −1, −2, a total of five. We find from table 10.1, however, that under the $M_s = 0$ states there are nine entries. The four additional to those originating from ^1D are attributable to ^1S and ^3P, the latter taking the values $M = 1, 0, −1$ and $M_s = 1, 0, −1$. There are nine entries for ^3P, five for ^1D and one for ^1S. In table 10.2 some results for other electronic configurations are given.

11   Electron–Electron Repulsion in Atoms

In § 10, atomic states were classified by the *LS* or *Russell–Saunders* scheme. As mentioned in § 8, the states of a given configuration are calculated to be degenerate if the Hamiltonian of equation (6.2) is employed. For atoms of low atomic number the most significant of the absent terms in the Hamiltonian are those of the form $\hat{q} = e^2/r_{ij}$, the electron–electron repulsion terms.

Because $\hat{q}$ is a two-electron operator (involving electrons i and j), an integral of the form $\langle \Psi_a | \hat{q} | \Psi_b \rangle$ is nonzero only if not more than two of the components in Ψ_a (equation (8.1)) are different from those of Ψ_b. The most general form of the integral is therefore

$$\langle \phi_a(1)\phi_b(2)|\hat{q}|\phi_c(1)\phi_d(2)\rangle = \langle ab|\hat{q}|cd\rangle. \tag{11.1}$$

This integral is zero unless the spin components of a and c are the same; similarly, the spins of b and d must be the same. The commutation of $\hat{q}$ and $\hat{S}_z$ accounts for this result. Thus if b has positive spin and d has negative spin (denoted $\bar{d}$) then $b = \phi_b\alpha$ and $\bar{d} = \phi_d\beta$,

$$\langle b|\hat{q}|\bar{d}\rangle = \langle\phi_b|\hat{q}|\phi_d\rangle\langle\alpha|\beta\rangle$$

and the integral $\langle\alpha|\beta\rangle = 0$.

Another important condition to be fulfilled in order that the integral of equation (11.1) be nonzero is

$$m_l^a + m_l^b = m_l^c + m_l^d. \tag{11.2}$$

These two conditions mean that there are nonzero integrals only between functions having the same values of M_L and M_S; for example, only between functions on the same horizontal row and in the same vertical column in table 10.1 Reference to table 10.1 will also help to clarify the next point; that the elements encountered in practice are of the form

$$\langle ab|\hat{q}|ab \rangle = J$$

$$\langle ab|\hat{q}|ba \rangle = K$$

where J and K are the *Coulomb* and *exchange* integrals, respectively. For example, consider the $(1^+, 0^+)$ term. This is one of the nine components of ^3P, and since they all have the same energy within this approximation, the evaluation of its energy is enough to fix the energy of ^3P. Written as a Slater determinant,

$$\Psi(^3P) = \frac{1}{\sqrt{2}}\begin{vmatrix} 1^+(1) & 0^+(1) \\ 1^+(2) & 0^+(2) \end{vmatrix}$$

$$\langle \Psi|\hat{q}|\Psi \rangle = \tfrac{1}{2}\langle 1^+(1)0^+(2) - 1^+(2)0^+(1)|\hat{q}|1^+(1)0^+(2) - 1^+(2)0^+(1) \rangle$$

$$= \tfrac{1}{2}(J + J - K - K)$$

$$= J - K. \tag{11.3}$$

The calculation of $\langle ab|\hat{q}|bc \rangle$ is facilitated by the general result

$$\langle ab|\hat{q}|cd \rangle = \sum_k c_k(ac)c_k(bd)R_k(ac, bd) \tag{11.4}$$

where the $c_k(ac)$ are coefficients dependent on the l and m_l quantum numbers of orbital a and the corresponding l' and m_l' of c (table 11.1). The R_k depend on the form assumed for the ϕ orbitals. The integer k is limited by the conditions

$$k + l + l' = 2g \text{ (}g \text{ integral)}$$

$$|l - l'| \leq k \leq |l + l'|.$$

Conventionally, $R_k(ab, ab)$ is written F_k, and $R_k(ab, ba)$ is written G_k if $a \neq b$ (that is, if the quantum numbers of a and b are different). If $a = b$, then $F_k = G_k$ and F_k is written; the two electrons are then said to be *equivalent*.

The energies of the terms deriving from the p^2 configuration with equivalent electrons can be written down from the foregoing. From table 10.1,

$$^1D = (1^+, 1^-) \tag{11.5}$$

$$^3P = (1^+, 0^+) \tag{11.6}$$

$$^1D + {}^3P + {}^1S = (1^+, -1^-) + (1^-, -1^+) + (0^+, 0^-). \tag{11.7}$$

The electron–electron repulsion energy of ^3P is, from equation (11.3),

$$J - K = \sum_k c_k(1^+1^+)c_k(0^+0^+)F_k - \sum_k c_k^2(1^+0^+)F_k$$

$$= (F_0 - 2F_2) - (3F_2)$$

$$= F_0 - 5F_2.$$

Table 11.1. $c_k(lm_l,\ l'm_l')$ coefficients for s, p and d electrons.

	m_l	$m_{l'}$	$k=0$	$k=1$	$k=2$	$k=3$	$k=4$
ss	0	0	1	0	0	0	0
sp	0	±1	0	-1	0	0	0
	0	0	0	1	0	0	0
pp	±1	±1	1	0	-1	0	0
	±1	0	0	0	$\sqrt{3}$	0	0
	±1	∓1	0	0	$-\sqrt{6}$	0	0
	0	0	1	0	2	0	0
sd	0	±2	0	0	1	0	0
	0	±1	0	0	-1	0	0
	0	0	0	0	1	0	0
pd	±1	±2	0	$-\sqrt{6}$	0	$\sqrt{3}$	0
	±1	±1	0	$\sqrt{3}$	0	$\frac{-3}{\sqrt{18}}$	0
	±1	0	0	-1	0	$\sqrt{18}$	0
	±1	∓1	0	0	0	$-\sqrt{30}$	0
	±1	∓2	0	0	0	$\sqrt{45}$	0
	0	±2	0	0	0	$\sqrt{15}$	0
	0	±1	0	$-\sqrt{3}$	0	$-\sqrt{24}$	0
	0	0	0	2	0	$\sqrt{27}$	0
dd	±2	±2	1	0	$\frac{-2}{\sqrt{6}}$	0	1
	±2	±1	0	0	$\sqrt{6}$	0	$-\sqrt{5}$
	±2	0	0	0	-2	0	$\sqrt{15}$
	±2	∓1	0	0	0	0	$-\sqrt{35}$
	±2	∓2	0	0	0	0	$\sqrt{70}$
	±1	±1	1	0	1	0	-4
	±1	0	0	0	1	0	$\sqrt{30}$
	±1	∓1	0	0	$-\sqrt{6}$	0	$-\sqrt{40}$
	0	0	1	0	2	0	6

For ^{1}D we have only the J term because the spins are unpaired,

$$J = \sum_k c_k(1^+1^+)c_k(1^-1^-)F_k$$

$$= F_0 + F_2.$$

Finally, for ^{1}S we evaluate the three terms of equation (11.7) and subtract from their sum the sum of the results for ^{1}D and ^{3}P. The results are

$$\left.\begin{array}{l} ^1\text{D} = F_0 + F_2 \\[4pt] ^3\text{P} = F_0 - 5F_2 \\[4pt] ^1\text{S} = F_0 + 10F_2 \end{array}\right\}. \tag{11.8}$$

The average energy of the terms, taking their degeneracy of $2L+1$ into account, is F_0. In addition, a term E_0 has to be added to equations (11.8) to account for the paired electrons. Thus $^1\text{D} = E_0 + F_0 + F_2$. The average energy is now $E_0 + F_0$.

The above is called the *diagonal sum method*; it depends upon the *diagonal sum rule* that the sum of the energies of a number of terms such as those in equations (11.8) above is equal to the sum of the *diagonal matrix elements*. These are the J and K integrals for the sets of terms with the same values of M_L and M_S, such as the terms listed in equation (11.7).

Further information can be found in Slater (1960) and Condon and Shortley (1964).

12   Slater Orbitals

Exact atomic wavefunctions have the disadvantage of being complicated. This is true even for the simplest of them, the hydrogenic functions, which were discussed in § 6. The Slater functions described in this section are easy to write down, and although they are approximations they nevertheless provide a starting point for molecular calculations and they can provide much useful information, such as approximate values of overlap integrals.

Slater's orbitals are of the form of equation (6.3) but the radial function is

$$R(r) = cr^{(n^*-1)} \exp[-(Z-s)r/n^*] \qquad (12.1)$$

where c is a normalising constant, r is the distance from the nucleus in units of *Bohr radii* (0·5292 Å), Z is the atomic number, s is the *screening constant*, and n^* is the effective principal quantum number (cf equation (4.3)) given by the following 'Slater's rules'.

Rule 1: Orbitals are divided into the following groups:

$$1s \quad 2s, 2p \quad 3s, 3p \quad 3d \quad 4s, 4p \quad 4d \quad 4f.$$

Rule 2: For an electron in one of the above groups the screening constant is made up as follows.
(*a*) From electrons outside the group, nothing.
(*b*) From every electron in the same group, 0·35. If the group happens to be 1s, the value 0·3 is used.
(*c*) For an s or a p orbital, 0·85 for every electron in the group just below the one considered, and 1·0 for every electron lower still.
(*d*) For a d or an f orbital, 1·0 for every electron in a lower group.

Rule 3: n^* is assigned according to the value of the principal quantum number;

$$n = 1 \quad 2 \quad 3 \quad 4 \quad\quad 5 \quad 6$$
$$n^* = 1 \quad 2 \quad 3 \quad 3{\cdot}7 \quad 4 \quad 4{\cdot}2.$$

The screening effect of the inner electrons causes the true function to be larger and less concentrated about the nucleus than the hydrogen-like functions; the hydrogen-like O(2p) function is $cr \exp(-4r)$, whereas the Slater function is $cr \exp(-2{\cdot}28r)$. The more accurate Morse function for O(2p) is $cr \exp(-2{\cdot}22r)$. Slater showed that the term with the highest power of r in the radial function was the most important and Slater orbitals include only this one. Consequently there are too few radial nodes in some Slater orbitals; for example, for O(3s) the hydrogen function is

$$c(6 - 32r + 28{\cdot}44r^2) \exp(-2{\cdot}67r)$$

and the Slater function is

$$cr^2 \exp(-0{\cdot}3r).$$

It is therefore found that the ns functions are not orthogonal to one another. However the angular parts of the functions assure the orthogonality of s to p, p to d, etc. Above the value $n = 3$, Slater's orbitals are inaccurate and they should be used with caution above $n = 4$.

The 'size' of an atomic orbital can be defined as the distance from the nucleus where the function $\langle \psi | 4\pi r^2 | \psi \rangle$ reaches its maximum value, and for Slater orbitals (in units of Bohr radii) this is

$$(n^*)^2/(Z-s) \tag{12.2}$$

and the energy of the Slater orbitals is

$$-R(Z-s)^2/(n^*)^2. \tag{12.3}$$

Ionisation energies can be calculated from equation (12.3). Taking oxygen as an example, three processes can be defined:

$$h\nu + O(1s^2 2s^2 2p^4) \rightarrow O^+(1s^1 2s^2 2p^4) \tag{12.4}$$

$$h\nu + O(1s^2 2s^2 2p^4) \rightarrow O^+(1s^2 2s^1 2p^4) \tag{12.5}$$

$$h\nu + O(1s^2 2s^2 2p^4) \rightarrow O^+(1s^2 2s^2 2p^3). \tag{12.6}$$

The ionisation energy of process (12.4) is $E(M) - E(M^+)$, where

$$E(M) = 2E(1s) + 2E(2s) + 4E(2p)$$

$$= 1612 + 141 + 281 \text{ eV};$$

$$E(M^+) = E(1s) + 2E(2s) + 4E(2p)$$

$$= 870 + 198 + 396 \text{ eV}.$$

Hence the ionisation energy of $O(1s) = 2034 - 1464 = 570$ eV. The ionisation energy observed is in the region of 532 eV (the x-ray absorption edge lies at this energy). It is instructive to analyse the calculated ionisation energy into parts due to the 1s, 2s and 2p shells. Thus for the 2s shell we have $141 - 198 = -57$ eV; for the others the values are 742 eV (1s) and -115 eV (2p).

It is clear from the above that although it is the 1s shell that is ionised, the electrons in the other shells are also changed in energy and that this is partly a consequence of the loss of the screening effect of the photoelectron. As the photoelectron leaves the atom the effective nuclear charge increases and the remaining electrons 'relax' to lower energies. This relaxation energy reduces the magnitude of the ionisation energy substantially. It is as though the relaxation process 'squeezes out' the photoelectron with an extra 172 eV of energy.

Slater's rules gather together the 2s and 2p electrons in the same group, and consequently their ionisation energies are both calculated by the preceeding method to be 14 eV. The lowest ionisation energy of O is in fact 13·61 eV, where a 2p electron is removed to leave the ion in its ^4S state. The ion $O^+(1s^2 2s^2 2p^3)$ also has a ^{2}D state, with a corresponding ionisation energy of 16·86 eV, and a ^{2}P state with an ionisation energy of 18·54 eV. There are nine ionisation energies arising from the loss of the 2s electron, the average being around 35 eV.

13   The Variation Method

The variational treatment of eigenvalue problems was first used in quantum mechanics to calculate the ground state of helium. The basis of the method is simple; if the energy can be expressed as a function of some variable, say F, then the best value of F is that giving the minimum energy. In other words, the best value is that for which $dE/dF = 0$.

Let us apply the variation method generally to the problem of the relationship between the energy and the size of the orbital. Suppose the linear dimensions of an orbital are uniformly shrunk by the factor $1/F$ so that the wavelength associated with the electron becomes λ/F. The hypothesis of de Broglie (§ 5) tells us that the kinetic energy increases by F^2 and the potential energy (given by the second term in equation (6.2)) increases by the factor F. The relationship between total energy and linear dimension is therefore

$$E = BF^2 + CF \tag{13.1}$$

where B and C are constants.

Applying the variation theorem it is found that for the minimum value for the energy, $E = -BF^2$, and that at this energy, $C = -2BF$. Hence, at the minimum energy,

$$\text{total energy} = -(\text{kinetic energy});$$

$$\text{potential energy} = -2(\text{kinetic energy}).$$

These results are known as the *virial theorem*.

Let us now apply the variation theorem to the helium atom. The electronic configuration is 1s^2 and the unnormalised hydrogenic wavefunction, serving as a first approximation, gives

$$\Psi_1 = \exp(-Z'r_1)\exp(-Z'r_2) \tag{13.2}$$

where Z' (the variational parameter) is the effective nuclear charge and r_1 is the distance between electron number one and the nucleus. For a single electron, the Hamiltonian is given by equation (6.2), but the term for the kinetic energy can be written

$$-\tfrac{1}{2}\nabla^2 = -\frac{h^2}{8m\pi^2}\left(\frac{d^2}{dx^2} + \frac{d^2}{dy^2} + \frac{d^2}{dz^2}\right) \tag{13.3}$$

which derives from equation (5.1). The total Hamiltonian (excluding spin–orbit interaction) is

$$H = -\tfrac{1}{2}(\nabla_1^2 + \nabla_2^2) - \frac{Ze^2}{r_1} - \frac{Ze^2}{r_2} + \frac{e^2}{r_{12}}. \tag{13.4}$$

When $\langle \Psi_1 | H | \Psi_1 \rangle$ is calculated, the value of Z' for the minimum E is found to be 1·6875, compared with $Z' = 1·7$ for the Slater orbital.

The term e^2/r_{12} in the Hamiltonian is the electron–electron repulsion energy and it keeps the electrons further apart than they would be without it. Its effect on the wavefunction is to increase the screening constant, and it is evident that the Slater function is adapted to include this term. A large screening constant implies a large orbital in which the electrons are further apart. The limitations of the Slater functions are evidently connected with the inability of a single constant to account for both electron–electron and nuclear–electron types of interaction. A better function is

$$\Psi_2 = (1 + br_{12})\Psi_1$$

where b is an extra parameter. The larger b is, the more the electrons avoid each other. The optimum values of the constants of Ψ_2 are $b = 0·193$ Å, $Z' = 1·849$, and the ionisation energy of He($1s^2$) is calculated to be within 1·4% of the correct value. The incorporation of more parameters (as many as 14 have been used) gives a calculated value within experimental error of the observed value.

14 Self-Consistent Fields

Related to the variation method is Hartree's *self-consistent-field* technique. The starting point is the wavefunction of equation (8.1), where the ϕ functions are chosen to be simple; Slater functions are often used. From the discussion of the helium atom in § 13 it appears that better ϕ functions would include a term in r_{ij} in order to take account of electron correlation, although this introduces much complication into the integrals that have to be solved. The polyelectronic Hamiltonian,

$$H = \sum_i \left(-\tfrac{1}{2}\nabla_i^2 \frac{-Ze^2}{r_i} \right) + \sum_i \sum_{j<i} \frac{e^2}{r_{ij}} \qquad (14.1)$$

taken with the Ψ of equation (8.1), implies that the potential field in which the electrons of an atom move is

$$V_i = \frac{-Ze^2}{r_i} + \sum_{j<i} \left\langle \phi_j \left| \frac{e^2}{r_{ij}} \right| \phi_i \right\rangle. \qquad (14.2)$$

Assuming that Ψ is normalised, the energy is

$$E = \left\langle \Psi \left| \sum_i (-\tfrac{1}{2}\nabla_i^2 + V_i) \right| \Psi \right\rangle. \qquad (14.3)$$

Hartree's procedure is firstly to choose ϕ such that V_i can be evaluated by equation (14.2) and then, using V_i, to evaluate a new solution to equation (14.3). This is repeated until there is no change in V_i, which is then called a self-consistent field (SCF). There are two shortcomings to this: the lack of a proper method of taking electron correlation into account, and the failure to include the possibility of electron exchange.

Electron exchange can be incorporated by using a Slater determinant in place of equation (8.1) for Ψ. This makes no difference for a case like that of $He(1s^2)$, but in $He(1s^12s^1)$, for example, exchange terms can appear as discussed in § 11. Thus, if

$$\Psi = \frac{1}{\sqrt{2}}\begin{vmatrix} 1s(1) & 2s(1) \\ 1s(2) & 2s(2) \end{vmatrix}$$

the energy is

$$E = \epsilon(1s) + \epsilon(2s) + \tfrac{1}{2}\{\langle 1s(1)2s(2) - 1s(2)2s(1)|\hat{q}|1s(1)2s(2) - 1s(2)2s(1)\rangle\}$$

$$= \epsilon(1s) + \epsilon(2s) + J - K$$

where ϵ represents the one-electron orbital energies in the absence of electron–electron repulsion. With the incorporation of a Slater determinant the Hartree method is called the *Hartree–Fock* method.

The repulsive forces between electrons give correlations of two kinds; radial correlation and angular correlation. Radial correlation leads to one electron being far from the nucleus (*r* large), whilst the other is close (*r* small), and this is partly taken into account in Slater's orbitals. Angular correlation between electrons *i* and *j* depends on the angle between r_i and r_j. It is possible to incorporate angular correlation into the Hartree–Fock treatment of helium; for example, by mixing some other configurations containing p, d and f character into the $1s^2$ configuration; this is called *configuration interaction*.

Hylleraas obtained for helium a six-term wavefunction which can be assumed to be close to the true function using the method of § 13. It can be analysed into contributions of different *l* quantum numbers as follows.

	c^2	Energy contribution (eV)
s	0·99508	77·8753
p	0·00479	0·9506
d	0·00108	0·0650
f	0·000012	0·0150

The *c* coefficients are those of the configuration in the mixed wavefunction

$$\Psi = c_1(1s^2) + c_2(1s^12p^1) + \ldots \tag{14.4}$$

The use of 20 configurations in equation (14.4) produced a total energy of 78·9260 eV, which is poor compared with the Hylleraas solution (78·939 eV), but better than the Hartree result of 77·80 eV. The experimental value for helium is 78·9521 eV.

In figure 14.1 ionisation energies measured for the elements by Siegbahn and his colleagues (Siegbahn *et al* 1967) are plotted with the orbital energies calculated by the Hartree method (Herman and Skillman 1963), against the atomic number. It is clear from this figure that the ionisation energy is approximately equal in magnitude to the orbital energy

$$I(\Psi_i) \simeq -E(\Psi_i). \tag{14.5}$$

It is 'Koopmans' theorem' that the Hartree–Fock energy is equal in magnitude to the ionisation energy, but this approximation neglects the relaxation energy discussed in §§ 12 and 15. Nevertheless, it will often be convenient to equate ionisation energies with orbital energies.

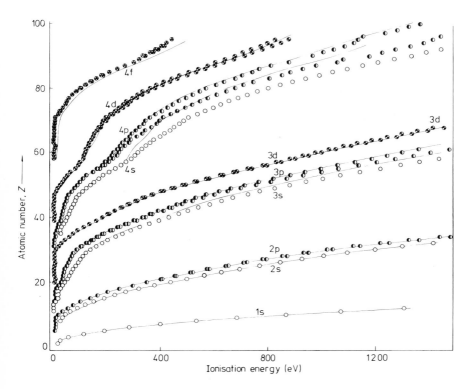

Figure 14.1. The energies of atomic orbitals (lines) calculated by the Hartree method (Herman and Skillman 1963), and the ionisation energies measured by x-ray photoelectron spectroscopy (circles) using Al Kα radiation (1487 eV) and Mg Kα radiation (1254 eV) (Siegbahn *et al* 1967). The experimental ionisation energies depend on the chemical form of the element, and these vary by a few electron volts. ○, s; ◐, p; ◑, d; ●, f.

In figure 14.2 the radial charge distribution calculated by the Hartree–Fock method for $Rb^+(1s^2 2s^2 2p^6 3s^2 3p^6 3d^{10} 4s^2 4p^6)$ is plotted against distance from the nucleus. The shells of $n = 1, 2$ and 3 are evident, but the uncompleted shell of $n = 4$ is not so prominent. It is interesting to compare the positions of maximum density for the atomic orbitals in figure 14.2 with those calculated by equation (12.2); 0·03 (1s), 0·12 (2s and 2p), 0·35 (3s and 3p), 0·56 (3d) and 1·7 (4s and 4p) in units of Bohr radii.

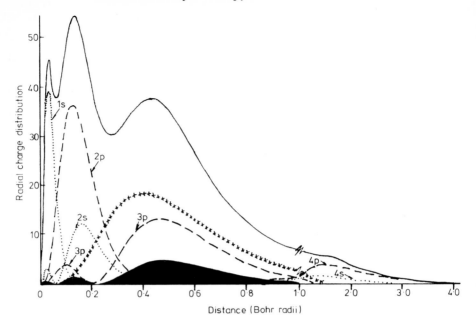

Figure 14.2. Radial charge distribution of Rb$^+$ calculated by the Hartree–Fock method, plotted against distance from the nucleus in units of Bohr radii (Mott and Sneddon 1948). ——— total; · · · s; – – – p; × × × 3d; shaded area, 3s.

15   Atomic Relaxation Energy

Koopman's theorem, introduced in § 14, is a 'frozen approximation', in which the electronic orbitals are treated as though they were unchanged or 'frozen' during ionisation. The total electronic energy of a system is

$$E(\text{total}, M) = E(\text{HF}) + E(\text{correlation}) + E(\text{relativistic}). \tag{15.1}$$

$E(\text{HF})$ is the sum of all the one-electron Hartree–Fock energies discussed in § 14; similarly, $E(\text{correlation})$ contains all the correlation energies. The important part of $E(\text{relativistic})$ is the spin–orbit interaction, which increases in magnitude with the atomic number. The ionisation energy is

$$I_i = \Delta E(\text{HF}) + \Delta E(\text{correlation}) + \Delta E(\text{relativistic}). \tag{15.2}$$

According to Koopmans' theorem, $I_i = -E_i$, where E_i is the ith one-electron Hartree–Fock energy, but if we write

$$I_i = -E_i + E(\text{relaxation}) + \Delta E(\text{correlation}) + \Delta E(\text{relativistic}) \tag{15.3}$$

then we can calculate $E(\text{relaxation})$ by the Hartree–Fock method, since

$$E(\text{relaxation}) = \Delta E(\text{HF}) + E_i. \tag{15.4}$$

Table 15.1. Atomic relaxation energies, E(relaxation), of equation (15.4) (in eV) (Gelius and Siegbahn 1972). Some of these values are interpolations.

	1s	2s	2p	3s	3p	3d	4s
	Non-relativistic calculations						
H	0·0						
He	1·5						
Li	3·8	0·0					
Be	7·0	0·7					
B	10·6	1·6	0·7				
C	13·7	2·4	1·6				
N	16·6	3·0	2·4				
O	19·3	3·6	3·2				
F	22·0	4·1	3·8				
	Relativistic calculations						
F	22·1	4·1	3·9				
Ne	24·8	4·8	4·7				
Na	23·3	4·1	4·7	0·3			
Mg	24·6	5·2	6·0	0·7			
Al	26·1	6·1	7·1	1·0	0·2		
Si	27·1	7·0	8·0	1·1	0·5		
P	28·3	7·8	8·8	1·2	0·7		
S	29·5	8·5	9·6	1·4	0·9		
Cl	30·7	9·3	10·4	1·5	1·1		
Ar	31·8	9·9	11·1	1·8	1·4		
K	31·2	9·1	10·5	2·3	1·9		
Ca	32·0	9·6	11·1	2·7	2·4		
Sc	33·8	11·5	12·9	3·2	2·9		
Ti	35·4	13·0	14·4	3·6	3·4	2·0	0·3
V	37·0	14·5	16·0	4·1	3·9	2·6	
Cr	38·6	15·9	17·4	4·6	4·3	3·2	
Mn	40·1	17·2	18·8	5·1	4·8	3·6	0·4
Fe	41·6	18·5	20·2	5·7	5·3	3·8	
Co	43·2	19·8	21·6	6·2	5·8	4·1	0·0
Ni	44·7	21·1	22·9	6·7	6·3	4·5	
Cu	48·2	23·7	25·7	7·7	7·2	5·3	0·3

Thus defined, E(relaxation) lacks the component due to correlation and it is a negative quantity. Calculated values are given in table 15.1.

The sequence of ionisation energies in a spectrum is very often the same as the sequence of orbital energies, the relaxation energies being either of much the same magnitude or at any rate insufficiently different to alter the order of appearance of the bands. In many cases, however, there is a difference in the sequence; for example, in ferrocene, the nitrogen molecule and cyanogen.

In molecules, as opposed to atoms, there is a component of E(relaxation) due to the rearrangement of charge amongst the atomic orbitals comprising the molecular orbitals. In *bis*-(π-allyl) nickel, the orbital of lowest ionisation energy undergoes, upon ionisation, an increase in the percentage of Ni(3d) character; the calculated value increases from 62 to 96% (Rohmer and Veillard 1973). Although it has the lowest ionisation energy, this orbital falls short by some 9 eV from having the lowest bonding energy eigenvalue.

16   Problems

1   Germanium has the configuration (core) $4s^2 4p^2$. If $F_2 = 0\cdot126$ eV, show that the ground state is the triplet by calculating the separation of the ^1S, ^1D and ^3P terms due to electron–electron repulsion. Show that the interval ratio $(^1S - {}^1D):({}^1D - {}^3P)$, expected from the same cause is $3:2$.

2   Show that in the case of a pair of non-equivalent p electrons such as $2p^1 3p^1$, there is a ^3D state from the (1^+1^+) combination and that the electron–electron repulsion energy is $F_0 + F_2 - G_0 - G_2$.

3   Show that the normalised Slater 1s orbital obeys

$$4\pi \int_0^\infty \psi^2 r^2 \mathrm{d}r = 1$$

and hence that $c = [(Z - s)^3 / \pi]^{1/2}$ in equation (12.1).

4   Calculate the ionisation energy of helium using the results that

(a) the energy of Ψ_1 (equation (13.2)), without any variation of Z, is $(2Z^2 - 5Z/4)R$, where Z is the nuclear charge;

(b) the energy of Ψ_1 when Z is allowed to vary is $(-2Z'^2 + 27Z'/4)R$, where Z' is the effective nuclear charge;

(c) the energy of He$(1s^1)$ is $Z^2 R$.

    Take the values, $R = 13\cdot6$ eV, $Z = 2$, and compare your results with the observed ionisation energy of $24\cdot58$ eV.

5   Show that for the ^3P state of carbon in the configuration $2s^2 2p^2$, the Hartree–Fock energy is

$$2\epsilon(2s) + 2\epsilon(2p) + J(2s, 2s) + J(2p, 2p) + 4J(2s, 2p) - 2K(2s, 2p)$$

and that for $C^+(2s^2 2p^1)$ the energy differs from the above by

$$\epsilon(2p) + J(2p, 2p) + 2J(2s, 2p) - K(2s, 2p)$$

which is the ionisation energy of the 2p electrons.

2 Molecular Orbitals

17 Hydrides Isoelectronic with Neon

In some molecules, such as hydrogen fluoride, molecular orbitals can be regarded as distorted atomic orbitals. The appropriate atomic orbitals in HF are those of the isoelectronic neon atom and the distortion is simply that due to the shift of unit positive charge from the nucleus to the position of the hydrogen atom, $0.918\,\text{Å}$ away. Evidently, the distortion consists of augmented electronic density in the region of the hydrogen atom where it is drawn by the attraction of the additional positive charge (figure 17.1). In the Hamiltonian an extra term appears, Ze^2/R_{ij}, to account for the nuclear–nuclear repulsion and there are extra terms, $-e^2/r_i$, one for every electron, to account for the additional electron–nuclear attractions.

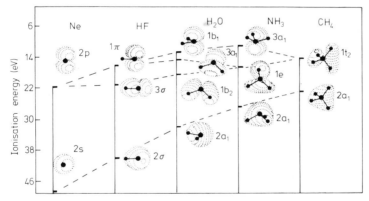

Figure 17.1. The electronic orbitals of some molecules isoelectronic with neon drawn as surfaces of constant electronic density (Jorgensen and Salem 1973). Nuclei are denoted by full circles and bonds by full lines. The ionisation energies are indicated by bold horizontal bars (Potts and Price 1972). The system of labelling consists in numbering orbitals of the same symmetry in the order of the energy. The symmetry labels are the irreducible representations of the point groups $C_{\infty v}$(HF), C_{2v} (H_2O), C_{3v} (NH_3) and T_d (CH_4).

In figure 17.1 the orbital of HF labelled 2σ is derived from the 2s orbital of Ne. The spherical symmetry of the atomic orbital gives way to the pear-shaped $C_{\infty v}$ symmetry of the molecular orbital. The ionisation energy of the molecular orbital is lower in magnitude than that of the atom because the division of the nuclear charge has caused the effective nuclear charge to diminish (equation (12.3)). The nuclear–nuclear repulsive force lowers the stability of the orbital. As one proceeds along the isoelectronic series HF, H_2O, NH_3, ..., the stability of the electronic orbitals continues to decrease, the least stable member being CH_4. No BH_5 is known.

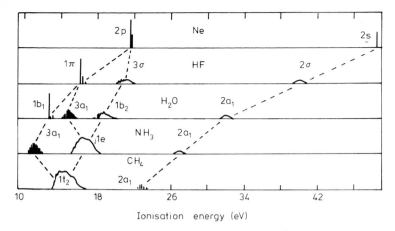

Figure 17.2. The photoelectron spectra of the hydrides of figure 17.1 obtained with He light (Potts and Price 1972). Related peaks are connected by broken lines.

The photoelectron spectra reveal this trend in a very clear way, as shown in figure 17.2.

As mentioned in § 4 the line spectrum of the atom becomes broadened into series of lines or bands in molecules. In figure 17.2 the lines in the photoelectron spectrum of Ne attributed to the 2p orbitals are split into two by the spin–orbit interaction. One of these components is twice as intense as the other, in accordance with triple degeneracy for the 2p group as a whole, that is, $2p_x$, $2p_y$ and $2p_z$. In HF one component, say $2p_z$, has a greatly different energy from the other pair because the hydrogen nucleus lies in one of its lobes instead of in a nodal plane. In HF the 1π molecular orbitals derive from the $2p_x$ and the $2p_y$ atomic orbitals of neon, their degeneracy remaining whilst the 3σ orbital derives from $2p_z$. The 1π orbitals of HF are non-bonding, that is, they are not directly involved in the H—F bond and only a few vibrational steps are present in the corresponding photoelectron peak. On the other hand, the 3σ orbital is a bonding orbital; it deploys a large amount of charge between the nuclei and consequently helps to overcome the repulsive force between them. According to the *Hellman–Feynman theorem* the forces between an electron and the other particles in a molecule follow the classical Coulombic law, and the only difficulty in making the calculations is a positional one; where are the particles to be situated? The answer lies in a solution of the wavefunction. Once the electronic distribution becomes known, the bonding power of the orbitals can be assessed. Clearly, in figure 17.1 the 2σ orbital of HF is another bonding one and the photoelectron spectrum possesses a broad and structureless hump attributable to it.

In water the degeneracy of the 2p atomic orbitals is completely lost. In one of the 2p-derived molecular orbitals, $1b_1$, both bonds lie in a nodal plane and it is non-bonding. In the spectrum, $1b_1$ appears as a short vibrational progression. From an inspection of figure 17.2 it would appear that a characteristic of non-bonding orbitals is a band of quasi-atomic appearance with one or just a few vibrational steps and nearly all the intensity in the first step. In § 28 this observation receives a ready explanation.

In ammonia, degeneracy reappears in the 1e orbitals and the upper $3a_1$ orbital is no longer non-bonding, although it is not very strongly bonding either. Finally, in methane the threefold degeneracy is restored. Evidence of degeneracy is to be found in the presence of three 'humps' in the $1t_2$ photoelectron band which are a consequence of the dynamic Jahn–Teller effect (§ 33).

18 Molecular Orbitals

Possibly the most direct evidence that we have for the existence of molecular orbitals comes from photoelectron spectroscopy; occupied orbitals in the molecule are found to have their characteristic peaks. Although the concept of the molecular orbital derives from that of the atomic orbital it is not usually possible to relate the two quite as simply as in § 17. For example, one could not speak of the valence orbitals of Li_2 as derived by the distortion of the orbitals of only one atom, if only because both atoms have an equal weight. Instead, it is possible to express them as *linear combinations* of atomic orbitals,

$$\Psi = \sum_i c_i \phi_i. \tag{18.1}$$

In the above expression it is to be understood that the ϕ_i orbitals can lie on different atoms, each atom supplying its proper quota of orbitals. The c_i coefficients define the sign and the magnitude of the contribution of every ϕ_i. Molecular orbitals share the orthogonality property of atomic orbitals

$$\langle \Psi_j | \Psi_k \rangle = \delta_{jk}$$

where δ_{jk} is zero unless $j = k$, in which case it is unity. The square of the atomic orbital coefficient, c_i^2, is the probability that the electron occupying Ψ is to be found in ϕ_i.

The molecular Hamiltonian contains terms of Coulombic repulsion between nuclei, $Z_i Z_j e^2 / R_{ij}$ and, of course, the introduction of more nuclei involves more electron–nuclear attraction terms.

As in the atomic case, the energy of an unnormalised Ψ is

$$E = \frac{\langle \Psi | H | \Psi \rangle}{\langle \Psi | \Psi \rangle}$$

$$= \frac{\sum_i \sum_j c_i c_j \langle \phi_i | H | \phi_j \rangle}{\sum_i \sum_j c_i c_j \langle \phi_i | \phi_j \rangle}. \tag{18.2}$$

According to the variation theorem the best values for the coefficients are those for which $dE/dc = 0$. By differentiating the above expression and inserting the variation condition,

$$\sum_i \sum_j c_i(H_{ij} - ES_{ij}) = 0$$

$$H_{ij} = \langle \phi_i | H | \phi_j \rangle$$

$$S_{ij} = \langle \phi_i | \phi_j \rangle. \tag{18.3}$$

The equations comprising (18.3) are called the *secular equations.* They have a solution (other than all coefficients = zero) only if the following *secular determinant* is zero:

$$\begin{vmatrix} H_{11} - E & H_{12} - ES_{12} & H_{13} - ES_{13} & \cdots \\ H_{21} - ES_{21} & H_{22} - ES_{22} & H_{23} - ES_{23} & \cdots \\ \vdots & & & \\ & & \text{etc.} & \end{vmatrix} = 0. \tag{18.4}$$

In equation (18.4) it is assumed that the ϕ orbitals are normalised.

It is possible to solve equation (18.2) by the self-consistent-field technique, as discussed in § 14, although for any but the simplest molecules the Hartree–Fock treatment cannot readily be carried through to completion. The reason for this is the large amount of computer time necessary to evaluate the matrix elements of equation (18.4), especially the J and K integrals of § 14 whose number rises with the fourth power of the number of ϕ orbitals. When it is recalled that the Hartree–Fock solutions for atoms are far from being exact the situation for molecules appears hopeless indeed, but there is no need for undue pessimism; qualitative or very approximate solutions are often sufficient for the assignment of spectra and even for an understanding of the chemical bonding. So many different methods are in vogue for the approximate solution of the secular equations that an account of them is beyond the scope of this book. However, a brief discussion is in order.

In the *Hückel method* the S_{ij} are ignored, although if they are all the same this makes no difference to the result since the H_{ij} are not evaluated mathematically but are treated as numerical parameters into which the effect of neglecting S_{ij} is subsumed. More importantly, H_{ij} is neglected unless the atoms upon which ϕ_i and ϕ_j lie are bonded to each other. Since the H_{ij} are not to be calculated in the Hückel method, the Hamiltonian is never defined and H_{ij} is just a number (in units of energy). If $i = j$, H_{ij} is often called the Coulomb integral, otherwise it is called the resonance integral. For more information see Streitweiser (1962) and Coulson *et al* (1965).

The Hückel method soon runs into difficulties if a number of different kinds of atomic orbitals are present. The reason for this is that empirical values have to be assigned to the parameters H_{ij}, etc, and it is not always easy to determine the most suitable values to be employed. In cases such as alternant hydrocarbons, where ϕ represents carbon 2p orbitals, this difficulty is not a great one. The Coulomb integrals can usually be set equal to the *valence orbital ionisation energy* (VOIE) in cases of difficulty (see Appendix III), and from them the resonance integrals can be derived as, for example,

$$H_{ij} = \tfrac{1}{2}kS_{ij}(H_{ii} + H_{jj}). \tag{18.5}$$

Often k takes the value 1·75 and the S_{ij} are evaluated using Slater orbitals. It is possible to perform cyclical calculations in which the charges, q_i, are calculated on every atom using the previous solution of Ψ and the parameters are then changed with a formula such as

$$\text{VOIE} = Aq^2 + Bq + C$$

where VOIE is the valence orbital ionisation energy, and A, B and C are constants. The calculation is repeated until convergence occurs, although sometimes it does not converge at all and successive results are wildly different.

More accurate calculations begin with the Hartree–Fock formalism. *Ab initio* methods employ either Slater-type orbitals for ϕ with the radial form

$$r^{n-1} \exp(-\alpha r)$$

where n is the principal quantum number, or Gaussian orbitals whose radial part is

$$r^{n-1} \exp(-\alpha r^2).$$

The advantage of the Gaussian orbitals is that the matrix elements require less time for their calculation, but since they are poorer approximations to the true atomic functions than Slater orbitals, two or more are required in the place of one Slater orbital. Some different choices of basis set in order of increasing refinement are set out below.

(1) 'Minimal basis sets' are inaccurate outside the first row of the periodic table. The orbitals included are 1s for hydrogen, and 1s, 2s and 2p for atoms from boron to fluorine. Typically, three Gaussian functions are used per orbital.
(2) 'Split valence shell' sets include the 1s orbitals from boron to fluorine, as four Gaussian functions, for example. The valence electrons are split into 'inner' and 'outer' components made up of separate Gaussian series of three terms or so.
(3) 'Polarisation basis sets' in which unoccupied orbitals are added to the foregoing sets. For example, 3d might be added to an oxygen set. Here allowance is being made for the distortion of the atomic orbital by the rest of the molecule.

When atoms from outside the first row of the periodic table are present the Hartree–Fock method becomes time-consuming, many hours being required even on the fastest computer. Additionally, the problem of storing the multitudinous two-electron integrals becomes acute. There is therefore a need for less expensive, if less accurate, methods and the following approximations are common.
(*a*) The 'valence electron approximation' treats the non-valence orbitals of the molecule as part of an unpolarisable core. The term in the Hartree–Fock Hamiltonian for nuclear attraction,

$$\sum_{\text{nuclei},\,\mu} Z_\mu e^2 / r_{i\mu},$$

becomes

$$\sum_{\mu} V_{\mu},$$

where the latter is the effective electrostatic field of the core written as a sum of the atomic terms. The nuclear–nuclear repulsion is

$$\sum_{\mu}\sum_{\nu} Z'_{\mu}Z'_{\nu}e^2/R_{\mu\nu},$$

where Z'_{μ} is the core charge of atom μ. This approximation leads to errors in the calculation of the charge distribution in the molecule.

(b) 'Neglect of diatomic differential overlap' implies the neglect of two-electron integrals involving $\langle ij\|kl\rangle$ unless i and j belong to the same atom μ, and k and l belong to the same atom ν. The approximation (a) above is also taken in addition to the assumption that $S_{ij} = \delta_{ij}$. This level of approximation is often abbreviated to NDDO.

(c) 'Complete neglect of differential overlap' is an extension of approximation (b) in that $\langle ij\|kl\rangle = 0$ unless $i = j$ and $k = l$, in addition to the above restrictions. Thus the integral

$$\langle 3p_{\mu}3d_{\mu}|e^2/r|3p_{\nu}3d_{\nu}\rangle$$

would be set equal to zero. These two-electron integrals are reduced to a constant, $\gamma_{\mu\nu}$, of average repulsion between an electron in a valence shell on μ, and another in a valence shell on ν. It is an approximation giving rather poor energies and is abbreviated to CNDO.

Since different methods often give quite different answers, it is useful for comparison to have compilations such as that of Snyder and Basch (1972), where the same method is employed for a number of molecules.

19   Examples of Molecular Orbital Calculations

As an example of the use of the Hückel method, let us choose H_2. The secular determinant is

$$\begin{vmatrix} \epsilon & 1 \\ 1 & \epsilon \end{vmatrix} = 0$$

where $\epsilon = (\alpha - E)/\beta$, α being H_{ii} and β being H_{ij}. The solution is $\epsilon = \pm 1$ or

$$E = \alpha \pm \beta. \tag{19.1}$$

The VOIE of H(1s) is 13·6 eV, and equating this with α we find a bonding orbital of ionisation energy $13·6 + \beta$ and an antibonding orbital of energy $13·6 - \beta$. The observed ionisation energy of H_2 is 15·422 eV and hence $\beta \approx 1·82$ eV. Equation (18.5) is wrong for s orbitals, since maximum overlap occurs for a bond length of zero. However, this remark is untrue for p orbitals; for N_2 the maximum 2p–2p overlap occurs at 1·22 Å and the observed nuclear separation is 1·10 Å.

Corresponding to equation (18.1) are the eigenfunctions

$$\Psi(\text{bonding}) = \frac{\phi_1(H_{1s}) + \phi_2(H_{1s})}{\sqrt{2}}$$

$$\Psi(\text{antibonding}) = \frac{\phi_1(H_{1s}) - \phi_2(H_{1s})}{\sqrt{2}}$$

which are obtained from the secular equations plus the normalisation condition. For more complex molecules such as H_2O, the arithmetic becomes formidable in the absence of a computer.

Table 19.1. Self-consistent-field calculations for water.

Orbital	Energy eigenvalue (eV)	I(calc)	I(observed)
$1b_1$	$13 \cdot 8^{[a]}$	$12 \cdot 34^{[b]}$	$12 \cdot 8$
$3a_1$	$15 \cdot 4$	$14 \cdot 68$	$14 \cdot 8$
$1b_2$	$19 \cdot 5$	$18 \cdot 85$	$18 \cdot 6$
$2a_1$	$37 \cdot 1$	$32 \cdot 34$	$32 \cdot 2$
$1a_1$	$559 \cdot 3$	$539 \cdot 6$	$539 \cdot 7$

[a] Snyder and Basch (1972).
[b] Meyer (1971).

Some typical self-consistent-field results for water are given in table 19.1. For the energy eigenvalue calculations the oxygen basis set consisted of four s components each made up of a series of Gaussians of the form $\exp(-\alpha r^2)$ and two p series made up of Gaussians of the form $x \exp(-\alpha r^2)$ for the x component and corresponding y and z components.

The more elaborate calculation of Meyer (1971) had eleven s, seven p, four d and one f Gaussians for the oxygen atom, plus five s and one p Gaussians for the hydrogen. To guide the choice of configurations, use was made of the fact that a large proportion of the correlation energy comes from interaction between pairs of electrons in the same orbital. When both ion and neutral molecule are included, the calculated ionisation energies here are so accurate that the question arises as to what experimental value they refer, the *vertical ionisation energy* given by the position of the peak height maximum, or this energy corrected for vibrational distortion. In table 19.1 the corrected values are given although the correction is small; for example, $0 \cdot 1$ eV for $3a_1$.

20 Hydrogen Fluoride

The electrostatic model of hydrogen fluoride is simply H^+F^-, the attraction between the charges providing the bond strength. If this were a correct picture, one electron being transferred from the H atom to the F atom, then the molecular dipole moment would be equal in magnitude to re^-, where r is the distance between the nuclei and e^- is the charge of the electron. The distance between the nuclei is known to be $0 \cdot 92$ Å, hence re^- is readily obtained, and it is found that the ratio (observed moment)/(calculated moment) is 0·43. Therefore only 0·43 of a complete electronic charge is transferred.

The result of the molecular orbital treatment of hydrogen fluoride is in agreement with the picture of a polarised molecule, $H^{\delta+}F^{\delta-}$, and the 2σ and the 3σ orbitals drawn in figure 17.1 contain a preponderance of fluorine character. This result is obtained without difficulty by means of a Hückel calculation along the lines of § 19.

The secular determinant for HF for the atomic orbitals H(1s), F(2s) and F(2p) is

$$\begin{vmatrix} F(2s) & H(1s) & F(2p) \\ (\epsilon + \Delta\epsilon_{2s}) & 1 & 0 \\ 1 & \epsilon & 1 \\ 0 & 1 & (\epsilon + \Delta\epsilon_{2p}) \end{vmatrix} = 0 \qquad (20.1)$$

where ϵ is the value of $(\alpha - E)/\beta$ for H(1s) and $\Delta\epsilon_{2s}$ is the increment between this value and the F(2s) value. Similarly, $\Delta\epsilon_{2p}$ is the increment for F(2p). By equating α with the VOIES of Appendix III, these 'diagonal elements' can be found once a value for β is assigned. The overlap integral between H(1s) and F(2p) has the approximate value of $\frac{1}{3}$ and equation (18.5) gives $\beta = 9\cdot4$. However, the value here assumed for β is 10 eV and the same will be assigned to the integral between H(1s) and F(2s). We now have

$$\epsilon = 13\cdot6 \text{ eV}$$

$$\Delta\epsilon_{2s} = 3\cdot28 \text{ eV}$$

$$\Delta\epsilon_{2p} = 0\cdot51 \text{ eV}$$

$$\beta = 10 \text{ eV}$$

and the secular determinant gives

$$\epsilon^3 + 3\cdot79\,\epsilon^2 - 0\cdot3272\,\epsilon - 3\cdot79 = 0. \qquad (20.2)$$

The solutions are

$$\epsilon = 0\cdot931, \ -1\cdot134 \quad \text{and} \quad -3\cdot587,$$

which give the energies

$$E = 4\cdot29, \ 24\cdot95 \quad \text{and} \quad 49\cdot47 \text{ eV}.$$

Because positive values have been assigned to α and β, the above are of the wrong sign for orbital energies, but are of the correct sign for ionisation energies. Thus the orbital of energy 4·29 eV is the least stable and is, in fact, unoccupied. For comparison, the results of an SCF calculation (Snyder and Basch 1972), using the same approximation as in table 19.1, are −5·78, 20·5 and 43·53 eV. The observed ionisation energies are plotted in figure 20.1.

The coefficients of the atomic functions in the molecular orbitals can now be calculated by substituting the values for ϵ in the secular equations. Thus, for $\epsilon = -1\cdot135$,

$$(-1\cdot135 + 3\cdot28)c(F_{2s}) + c(H_{1s}) = 0$$

$$c(H_{1s}) + (-1\cdot135 + 0\cdot51)c(F_{2p}) = 0$$

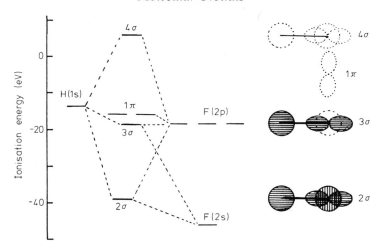

Figure 20.1. Energy diagram for HF. The ionisation energies were obtained from the photoelectron spectrum (Lempka *et al* 1968), and the energy of the unoccupied 4σ orbital was calculated by an SCF method with Koopman's approximation (Snyder and Basch 1972). For the atomic orbitals, VOIE values are given.

and with the normalisation condition

$$c^2(F_{2s}) + c^2(H_{1s}) + c^2(F_{2p}) = 1$$

we obtain

$$c(F_{2s}) = 0.240$$

$$c(H_{1s}) = -0.515$$

$$c(F_{2p}) = -0.824.$$

Since the charge density is proportional to the square of the coefficient, the charge distribution in this orbital has been found to be 5.76% F(2s), 26.52% H(1s) and

Table 20.1. Hückel calculations for HF and OH.

		HF		
Orbital	ϵ	$c(F_{2s})$	$c(H_{1s})$	$c(F_{2p})$
4σ	0.9313	0.191	−0.804	0.558
3σ	−1.135	0.240	−0.515	−0.824
2σ	−3.587	0.951	0.292	0.095
		OH		
	ϵ	$c(O_{2s})$	$c(H_{1s})$	$c(O_{2p})$
4σ	1.093	0.259	−0.770	0.582
3σ	−0.806	0.421	−0.453	−0.786
2σ	−2.397	0.869	0.449	0.207

67·90% F(2p). The remainder of these results are given in table 20.1. Summing the charge densities of the occupied orbitals we find 3·3 electrons in the fluorine orbitals of our basis set and 0·7 electrons in the H(1s) orbital; 1·3 electronic charges have been transferred. Comparison with the observed dipole moment of HF indicates that this is an over-estimate of the polarisation. The SCF technique referred to above also over-estimates polarisation, calculating that 0·54 electronic charges have been transferred.

The choice of basis orbitals for the Hückel calculation requires some comment since the F(1s) and two of the F(2p) orbitals have been ignored. The F(1s) orbital is left out on the grounds of energy; it lies at over 700 eV, it is smaller in radius than the valence orbitals, and consequently its overlap integral with them is small. The F(1s) orbital is included in the SCF calculation and is found to constitute less than 1% of the 3σ orbital, for example. The F(2p) orbitals that are left out are both perpendicular to the bond. Their overlap with H(1s) is zero in magnitude and their exclusion is a consequence of the molecular symmetry. On the Hückel level, the 1π orbitals are exclusively F(2p) and their energy is $-18\cdot7$ eV (the SCF calculation finds for them $-17\cdot5$ eV).

Where the overlap integral between atoms is positive there is an augmented electronic density and bonding as opposed to antibonding. Evidently, the 2σ orbital is bonding since all its coefficients in table 20.1 are of the same sign. 3σ appears to be bonding for F(2p) but antibonding for F(2s), whilst 4σ is antibonding for both. In antibonding orbitals a negative overlap is present, indicating a diminished

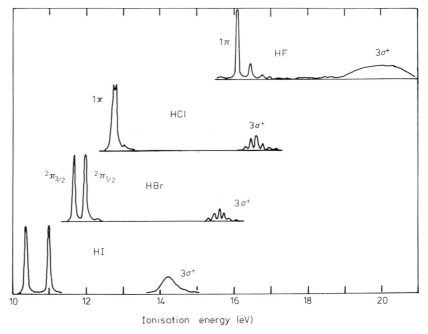

Figure 20.2. Photoelectron spectra of the hydrogen halides obtained using He resonance radiation (Lempka *et al* 1968).

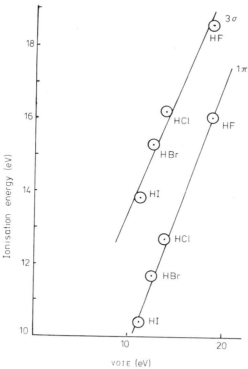

Figure 20.3. The ionisation energy of the hydrogen halide 3σ and 1π orbitals plotted against the halogenic p orbital energy (VOIE) of Appendix III.

electronic charge between nuclei. A measure of the amount of electronic charge lying between nuclei is

$$c_i c_j S_{ij}$$

which is called the *overlap population* when it is summed over all the electrons. For HF, the overlap populations—taking into account the fact that there are two electrons per orbital—are calculated to be (SCF) $0\cdot0000$ (1σ), $0\cdot1948$ (2σ), $0\cdot2662$ (3σ) and exactly zero (1π). The non-bonding nature of the 1π orbital is denoted by its overlap population of zero.

Hückel results for OH are also given in table 20.1. The same method of calculation as for HF was used with $\beta = 10$ eV. The ionisation energy of 1π is predicted to be $15\cdot9$ eV (compare the value in problem 1, p 48). It is found that OH is less polar than HF, as would be expected from the relative electronegativities of O and F.

The photoelectron spectra of the halides of hydrogen are shown in figure 20.2. Spin–orbit splitting of the 1π band is only $0\cdot03$ eV in HF and is not resolved, but it becomes larger as the atomic number increases. A linear relationship is found (figure 20.3) between the ionisation energies of the 1π and the 3σ orbitals and the VOIES of the halogenic p orbital. This is attributable to the predominantly halogenic character of the orbitals.

21 Water

The angle between the hydrogen atoms in water is $104° 27'$ and the symmetry is that of the C_{2v} point group. Including only the occupied atomic orbitals, the basis set is

$$H_1(1s) \text{ on H atom 1}$$

$$H_2(1s) \text{ on H atom 2}$$

$$O(1s)$$

$$O(2s)$$

$$O(2p_x), O(2p_y) \text{ and } O(2p_z).$$

In the parlance of group theory the above comprises a *reducible representation* containing or *spanning* a number of *irreducible representations*. In order to analyse the reducible representation into its components the *character table* is useful; that for C_{2v} is given in table 21.1. The analysis is carried out firstly by finding the

Table 21.1. The C_{2v} character table.

	E	$C_2(z)$	$\sigma_v(xz)$	$\sigma_v'(yz)$	
A_1	1	1	1	1	z, x^2, y^2, z^2
A_2	1	1	-1	-1	R_z, xy
B_1	1	-1	1	-1	x, R_y, xz
B_2	1	-1	-1	1	y, R_x, yz

characters of the reducible representation under all the operations of the group, and secondly by finding the combination of irreducible representations whose characters add up to the characters of the reducible representation.

Since the Hamiltonian and the symmetry operators commute, the eigenfunctions of one are the eigenfunctions of the other. A choice of the above basis orbitals transforming as one of the irreducible representations makes up an eigenfunction of the operations of the group, and consequently it is also an eigenfunction of the Hamiltonian. Group theory thus enables the symmetries of the molecular orbitals to be found easily. Although it tells us nothing directly about energy it is frequently a great simplification to have the correct eigenfunctions in advance of an energy calculation.

To illustrate the analysis of a reducible representation, consider the basis set $p_x + p_y + p_z$. It is written as a vector,

$$\overbrace{p_x, p_y, p_z}$$

and the operation $C_2(z)$ transforms it into

$$\overbrace{-p_x, -p_y, p_z}.$$

The effect of the transformation has been to multiply the vector by a matrix and the operation can be represented by an equation

$$C_2(z)\ \underbrace{p_x, p_y, p_z} = \underbrace{p_x, p_y, p_z} \begin{vmatrix} -1 & 0 & 0 \\ 0 & -1 & 0 \\ 0 & 0 & 1 \end{vmatrix}.$$

The character is the sum along the leading diagonal: $-1-1+1=-1$. In total the characters are

E	$C_2(z)$	$\sigma_v(xz)$	$\sigma'_v(yz)$
3	-1	1	1

and this is seen in table 21.1 to be the sum of the characters of A_1, B_1 and B_2. Hence the irreducible representations A_1, B_1 and B_2 comprise the reducible set of the three p orbitals.

The basis set for water possesses the characters

E	$C_2(z)$	$\sigma(xz)$	$\sigma'(yz)$
7	1	3	5

if we decide to orientate the molecule with the axes in the directions shown in figure 21.1. One generally chooses the z axis to be that of the greatest symmetry. Table 21.1 enables us to see that the basis set spans $B_1+2B_2+4A_1$. There are four orbitals of A_1 symmetry, each distinguished by a number which increases as the orbital energy increases. Thus the electronic configuration is $(1a_1)^2(2a_1)^2(1b_2)^2(3a_1)^2(1b_1)^2$. There is a convention that states of molecules are

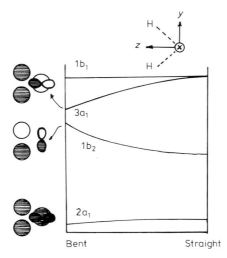

Figure 21.1. Walsh diagram for H_2O. The orbital energies were calculated by an SCF method for different values of the H–O–H angle. It is evident that the $3a_1$ orbital disposes towards nonlinear geometry and the $1b_2$ towards linear, the remainder being neutral in this respect, or nearly so. On the left the H(1s), O(2p) and O(2s) atomic orbitals are indicated. Where they are similarly shaded, the atomic orbitals are in phase in the molecular orbitals.

denoted with capital letters and orbitals with small letters. Thus the ionisation of the $3a_1$ orbital gives the $^2A_1$ state of the ion (alternatively written $3a_1^{-1}$).

The fact that water is a bent rather than a straight molecule must derive from the electron distribution. In figure 17.1 the $1b_1$ orbital is seen to be non-bonding and is therefore of no significance as far as the molecular angle is concerned. The $3a_1$ orbital is derived from the $2p_z$ orbital of the oxygen atom and it would be non-bonding if the molecule were linear. In the bent geometry, one lobe of charge is deployed between the nuclei and therefore $3a_1$ is lowered in energy by the bending. On the other hand, $1b_2$ is bonding in either the linear or the straight molecule and since it derives from $2p_y$ it could be guessed that the maximum overlap and therefore the best bonding occurs with the linear shape. Since it is approximately spherical, the $2a_1$ orbital has a nearly neutral influence on shape.

The above considerations can be quantified by carrying out a series of energy calculations for different values of the bond angle. In figure 21.1 the orbital energies are plotted against the H–O–H angle and the above expectations are found to be realised. Diagrams such as figure 21.1 are known as *Walsh diagrams*.

O–H overlap populations calculated by the SCF method of table 19.1 (Snyder and Basch 1972) are zero ($1b_1$), 0·331 ($1b_2$), 0·0339 ($3a_1$), 0·2022 ($2a_1$) and −0·001 ($1a_1$). The $1b_1$ orbital is non-bonding and $1a_1$ is slightly antibonding; the latter is mainly O(1s). The H–H overlap populations are zero ($1a_1$ and $1b_1$), −0·1032 ($1b_2$), 0·0055 ($2a_1$) and 0·0253 ($3a_1$). The H–H overlap populations confirm that an

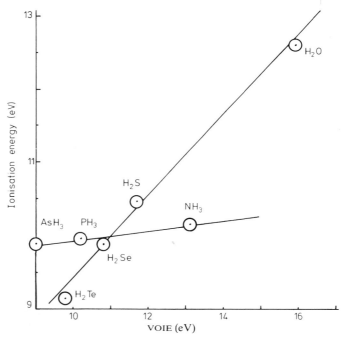

Figure 21.2. The ionisation energies of the lone-pair ($1b_1$) molecular orbitals of H_2S and its congeners plotted against the VOIES of the p orbitals of the heavy atom. Also plotted are the $3a_1$ ionisation energies of NH_3 and its congeners.

electron in the $1b_2$ orbital causes a repulsive force between the two H atoms since the overlap is negative in sign, whereas the $3a_1$ orbital has the opposite effect.

As in the hydrogen halides, a plot of the lone-pair ionisation energy against the heavy-atom VOIE is linear for the series H_2O, H_2S, ... (figure 21.2).

22   Ammonia

In the vapour state, ammonia takes the shape of a trigonal pyramid and belongs to the C_{3v} point group, the characters are given in table 22.1. The N–H distance is $1\cdot015$ Å and the H–N–H angle is $106\cdot6°$. The z axis of the molecule passes through the nitrogen atom, the xy plane being defined by the hydrogen nuclei (figure 22.1).

The symbol C_α means 'rotation by the angle α': for example, z is a threefold rotation axis, C_3, in ammonia. We shall take C_α to mean that *the axes are rotated by the angle α, the molecule being left unchanged*. A positive rotation takes the positive half of an axis, say $+x$ into the positive half of another, say $+y$. A right-handed system of axes is always chosen, that is, a positive rotation taking x into y advances along the positive direction of z if the motion is imagined as a right-hand screw.

Table 22.1. The characters for the point group C_{3v}.

	E	$2C_3(z)$	$3\sigma_v$	
A_1	1	1	1	z, x^2+y^2, z^2
A_2	1	1	-1	R_z
E	2	-1	0	$x, y, R_x, R_y, x^2-y^2, xz, yz$

Consider the effect of C_α† (figure 22.1) upon the p_x orbital. In table 6.1 the angular part of the orbital is given as $\sin\theta\cos\phi$, which has a maximum when $\phi=0$, as it must if the orbital is to lie along the x axis. Upon rotation of the axis by the angle α the maximum will occur when $\phi=-\alpha$, that is, the function becomes $\sin\theta\cos(\phi+\alpha)$. The effect of the rotation can be written

$$C_\alpha \sin\theta\cos\phi = \sin\theta\cos(\phi+\alpha)$$
$$= \sin\theta\cos\phi\cos\alpha - \sin\theta\sin\phi\sin\alpha$$
$$= p_x\cos\alpha - p_y\sin\alpha.$$

In a similar way, for p_y we have

$$C_\alpha p_y = p_x\sin\alpha + p_y\cos\alpha.$$

Expressing both of the above results together,

$$C_\alpha \widehat{p_x, p_y} = \widehat{p_x, p_y}\begin{pmatrix} \cos\alpha & \sin\alpha \\ -\sin\alpha & \cos\alpha \end{pmatrix}. \tag{22.1}$$

From equation (22.1) the character of the basis, p_x+p_y, for rotation about z by the angle α is $2\cos\alpha$. Hence, for the C_3 operation about z the character is $2\cos(120°)=-1$. In figure 22.1 the reflection operations of the group are also

† C_α here means a rotation by $\alpha°$.

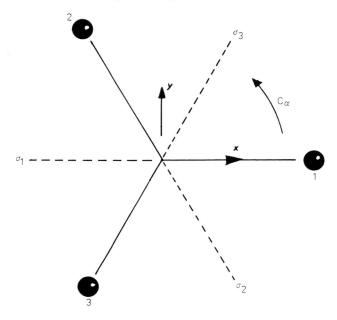

Figure 22.1. Operations for the point group C_{3v}. Mirror planes perpendicular to the paper are denoted σ_1, σ_2 and σ_3. In ammonia the **xy** plane is defined by the three hydrogen atoms drawn as full circles and **z** is the vertical axis.

defined. The matrices for reflection equivalent to equation (22.1) are

$$\overset{\sigma_1}{\begin{pmatrix} 1 & 0 \\ 0 & -1 \end{pmatrix}} \quad \overset{\sigma_2}{\begin{pmatrix} -1/2 & -\sqrt{3/2} \\ -\sqrt{3/2} & 1/2 \end{pmatrix}} \quad \overset{\sigma_3}{\begin{pmatrix} -1/2 & \sqrt{3/2} \\ \sqrt{3/2} & 1/2 \end{pmatrix}}.$$

The character for these reflections is zero.

Under the identity operation the matrix is the unit matrix

$$\begin{pmatrix} 1 & 0 \\ 0 & 1 \end{pmatrix}$$

and in all, the characters for the basis, $p_x + p_y$, are

$$\begin{array}{ccc} E & C_3 & \sigma_v \\ 2 & -1 & 0 \end{array}.$$

According to table 22.1 the above are the characters of the irreducible representation e. Hence we can say the $N(p_x)$ and $N(p_y)$ orbitals of ammonia span the irreducible representation e. Since this is a doubly degenerate orbital there must be at least two molecular orbitals with this symmetry, but there may be more depending on our choice of basis orbitals.

In addition to the orbitals already mentioned, the smallest basis set would contain $N(2s)$, $N(2p_z)$ and three hydrogen 1s orbitals. Only atomic orbitals of the same irreducible representation combine to form molecular orbitals. In table 22.1 it appears that $N(2p_z)$ and $N(2s)$ are of the same irreducible representation, a_1, and they mix together but form no part of the orbitals of e symmetry. The reducible representation composed of the three $H(1s)$ orbitals has the characters

$$\begin{array}{ccc} E & C_3 & \sigma_v \\ 3 & 0 & 1 \end{array}$$

which imply $a_1 + e$.

There are always as many molecular orbitals as there are atomic orbitals in the basis set. Together, $N(p_x)$, $N(p_y)$ and the three $H(1s)$ orbitals provide two pairs of molecular orbitals of e symmetry and a single one of a_1 symmetry. Additionally, $N(p_z)$ and $N(1s)$ provide two more of a_1 symmetry. The atomic orbital coefficients given in table 22.2 show how the atomic orbitals contribute to the molecular orbitals.

Table 22.2. Approximate atomic orbital coefficients (c_i in equation (18.1)) for the orbitals of ammonia calculated by the SCF method.

	Energy (eV)	$H_1(1s)$	$H_2(1s)$	$H_3(1s)$	$N(1s)$	$N(2s)$	$N(2p_x)$	$N(2p_y)$	$N(2p_z)$
$1a_1$	−422·3	0·00	0·00	0·00	1·00	0·00	0·00	0·00	0·00
$2a_1$	−31·16	0·19	0·19	0·19	−0·30	0·87	0·00	0·00	0·18
$3a_1$	−11·22	0·07	0·07	0·07	0·08	−0·30	0·00	0·00	0·94
$1e$	−16·97	0·00	0·43	−0·43	0·00	0·00	0·00	0·80	0·00
$2e$	9·34	0·49	−0·20	−0·20	0·00	0·00	0·80	0·00	0·00

The $1a_1$ orbital is exclusively $N(1s)$ in character (or very nearly so), and plays no part in the chemical bonding. In the $3a_1$ orbital there is about 88% of $N(2p_z)$ component (measured in terms of the electronic charge c_i^2) and it is not quite non-bonding, although it is often called the 'lone-pair' orbital. In the photoelectron spectrum (figure 17.2) the $3a_1^{-1}$ band is broader and more structured than the truly non-bonding orbitals of H_2O and HF. The overlap population for $3a_1$ is neverthe-less small (table 22.3).

The overlap populations show the $1e$ orbitals to be the most bonding as far as N—H is concerned, although there is some H—H antibonding character evidenced by the negative H—H overlap population. This would imply that the $1e$ orbitals favour the planar orientation as shown in the Walsh diagram (figure 22.2).

Table 22.3. Overlap populations for ammonia (values of $c_i c_j S_{ij}$ summed over electrons) (Snyder and Basch 1972).

	H_1–H_2	N–H
$1a_1$	0·00	0·00
$2a_1$	0·005	0·188
$3a_1$	0·002	0·011
$1e$	−0·078	0·479

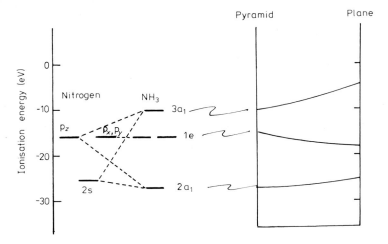

Figure 22.2. Energy diagram for ammonia showing the ionisation energies and the derivation of the orbitals. On the right is a Walsh diagram showing that the 1e orbitals favour the planar configuration, which is attributable to their H–H anti-bonding character.

Note: the reader proceeding logically through this book might now turn to Chapter 9 before reading Chapter 3.

Problems

1   The lowest ionisation energies of some hydrides are $16\cdot05$ eV (HF), $13\cdot01$ eV (OH), $12\cdot74$ eV (HCl), $11\cdot67$ eV (HBr) and $10\cdot38$ eV (HI). Show that the difference between these values and the VOIE of the heavy atom decreases with atomic number. Pauling gives the formula

$$I = 1 - e^{-1/4}(\chi_a - \chi_b)^2$$

for the charge on the atom, where χ_a is the electronegativity of atom a, and χ_b is the electronegativity of atom b. Show that there is an approximately linear relationship between I and the calculated differences. Electronegativity values are $2\cdot1$ (H), $4\cdot0$ (F), $3\cdot5$ (O), $3\cdot0$ (Cl), $2\cdot8$ (Br) and $2\cdot4$ (I).

2   From table 20.1 calculate the Hückel orbital energies of OH ($\alpha(O_{1s}) = 13\cdot6$ eV; $\beta = 10$ eV). Show that the values are not far from the ionisation energies of HF ($16\cdot0$, $18\cdot6$ and $39\cdot1$ eV). This can be explained as the result of the positive charge of the F atom which lowers its electronegativity towards that of O. Assuming that the HF values are appropriate for HNe, show why the latter is unstable.

3   In a linear molecule, angular momentum is quantised about the axis and the wavefunctions must therefore be eigenfunctions of the operator in equation (5.5). Show that $\Psi = \exp(\pm im\phi)$ are such functions, where ϕ is the angle in figure (5.1).

Show that the character of the pair of functions under the symmetry operation of rotation by the angle θ about the z axis is $2\cos(m\theta)$.

4 Some H—A bond distances (in ångströms) are: BeH_3^- (1·34); B_2H_6 (1·187 and 1·334); CH_3^+ (1·08); CH_2 (1·08); NH_3 (1·017); NH_2^- (1·03); H_2O (0·957) and, HF (0·917). Plot these against the following distances (in ångströms) for the maximum sigma overlap of H(1s) and the 2p orbitals. Li (1·35); Be (1·13); B (0·97); C (0·85), N(0·75), O(0·68), F (0·62). Predict the bond length in gaseous LiH. In solid LiH, which has the rock-salt structure, the observed distance is 2·04 Å, but here the structure is repeating units of LiH_6.

3 Vibrational Structure

23 The Nuclear Motion of Molecules

Compared with electrons, the molecular motions of nuclei are very slow and for some purposes they can be regarded as fixed in space. The *Franck–Condon principle*, for example, asserts that the nuclear geometry before and just after the photoelectric effect is the same, since molecular vibrations have a frequency of some 10^{-12} s and the photoelectric effect takes only about 10^{-15} s to complete.

A second but less rigorous principle, the *Born–Oppenheimer principle*, allows us to assume that the wavefunction of a molecule can be written as the product of an electronic function, $\psi(r, q)$, and a nuclear function, $\theta(q)$, where r is an electronic position vector and q is a nuclear displacement vector (giving the direction and magnitude of the displacement of a nucleus from the equilibrium position). So far as the Born–Oppenheimer principle is valid, a molecule can be in a variety of different vibrational states with one and the same electronic state.

Like electronic orbitals, vibrations can be labelled by the irreducible representations to which the molecule belongs. As an aid to the determination of the symmetry of vibrations use is made of *symmetry coordinates*. These are nuclear displacement vectors (there is one for every vibrating nucleus) which are chosen so

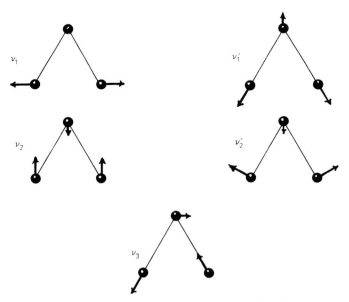

Figure 23.1. Symmetry coordinates of a triatomic molecule of C_{2v} symmetry. The lower, ν_3, is of b_1 symmetry and the rest are of a_1 symmetry.

that the set is an irreducible representation of the molecular point group (figure 23.1). In order to characterise genuine vibrations the set is chosen so that there is no rotation of the molecule as a whole and no motion of the centre of mass. With these restrictions, there are $3n-5$ vibrations for a linear molecule and $3n-6$ for a nonlinear one (where n is the number of nuclei). In molecular vibrations the nuclei oscillate at the same frequency in *normal modes* in which all nuclei pass through their maxima and minima together, that is, in phase, but with their own individual amplitudes.

In a heteronuclear diatomic molecule there is only one vibration ($3n-5=1$) and since it evidently has to belong to one of the irreducible representations of the $C_{\infty v}$ point group (table 23.1), it must be either σ^+ or σ^-, these being the only singly degenerate ones among them. However, σ^- represents a rotation of the molecule (R_z) and therefore the vibration is of σ^+ or a_1 symmetry. Such vibrations are called *totally symmetric* since the shape of the molecule is unaltered.

Table 23.1. The characters of the $C_{\infty v}$ point group.

	E	$2C_\infty^\phi$	$\infty\sigma_v$	
Σ^+	1	1	1	z, x^2+y^2, z^2
Σ^-	1	1	-1	R_z
Π	2	$2\cos\phi$	0	x, y, R_x, R_y, xz, yz
Δ	2	$2\cos 2\phi$	0	x^2-y^2, xy
ϕ	2	$2\cos 3\phi$	0	
$\cdots$	$\cdots$	$\cdots$	$\cdots$	
E_n	2	$2\cos n\phi$	0	

In most cases there is no unique choice of symmetry coordinates. Four possibilities are shown in figure 23.1 for the C_{2v} point group, although an infinite number of others exists. That there are a pair of normal vibrations of a_1 symmetry and one of b_1 symmetry in, for example, water, is shown by consideration of the irreducible representations of the C_{2v} point group spanned by the basis consisting of the nine nuclear displacement vectors. The latter arise by assigning three each to the nuclei (along x, y and z). The characters of the nine vectors are

E	$C_2(z)$	$\sigma_v(xz)$	$\sigma_v(yz)$
9	-1	3	1

In table 21.1 the sum of the characters for the three translations (x, y and z) and of the three rotations (R_x, R_y and R_z) is found to be

6	-2	0	0

and subtracted from the above it leaves

3	1	3	1

which are the characters of $2a_1+b_1$.

24   Simple Harmonic Motion

The simplest law of force for a stretched bond is Hooke's law:

$$\text{restoring force} = -kx \qquad (24.1)$$

where x is the change in bond length from its equilibrium value, and k is the force constant. Hooke's law is approximately true in many cases.

The molecule as a whole derives no momentum from a vibration. The dynamics of a two-particle system in which this condition is satisfied were analysed in § 2 and it is clear that the kinetic energy is

$$T = \tfrac{1}{2}mu^2 + \tfrac{1}{2}MU^2 = \frac{1}{2}\left(\frac{1}{M} + \frac{1}{m}\right)^{-1} V^2$$

$$= \tfrac{1}{2}\mu(dx/dt)^2. \qquad (24.2)$$

The reduced mass, μ, is

$$\left(\frac{1}{M} + \frac{1}{m}\right)^{-1}. \qquad (24.3)$$

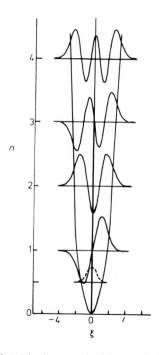

Figure 24.1. Plots of $\theta_n(\xi)$, the quantised harmonic function, against the bond length increment, ξ, for a diatomic molecule. Plots are given for different values of the vibrational quantum number, n. The parabola is a plot of the potential energy of the unquantised harmonic oscillator against ξ. The quantised functions extend beyond the range of the parabola, that is, larger bond length increments are permitted (see Problem 2, p 79).

The Hooke's law value for potential energy is

$$V = \tfrac{1}{2}kx^2. \tag{24.4}$$

The equation satisfying expression (24.1) is

$$x = a \cos(2\pi\nu t) \tag{24.5}$$

where a is a constant of the motion known as the amplitude. The frequency of the vibration is

$$\nu = (1/2\pi)(k/\mu)^{1/2} \tag{24.6}$$

and the vibrational Hamiltonian is

$$H = -\frac{h^2}{8\pi^2\mu}(d^2/dx^2) + \tfrac{1}{2}kx^2. \tag{24.7}$$

The solutions of equation (24.7) (Pauling and Wilson 1935) are

$$\theta_n(\xi) = \left[\frac{(\beta/\pi)^{1/2}}{2^n n!}\right]^{1/2} H_n(\xi)\exp(-\tfrac{1}{2}\xi^2) \tag{24.8}$$

$$\xi = \sqrt{\beta}x$$

$$\beta = (\mu k)^{1/2}(2\pi/h).$$

The functions symbolised by H_n are the Hermite polynomials of which the first few are

$$H_0(\xi) = 1$$
$$H_1(\xi) = 2\xi$$
$$H_2(\xi) = 4\xi^2 - 2$$
$$H_3(\xi) = 8\xi^3 - 12\xi$$
$$H_4(\xi) = 16\xi^4 - 48\xi^2 + 12.$$

It is noted that the powers of the Hermite polynomials are even when n is even, and odd when n is odd. The eigenvalues of equation (24.8) are

$$E_n = (n + \tfrac{1}{2})h\nu. \tag{24.9}$$

In figure 24.1 plots are given for two harmonic oscillators. The Hooke's law potential energy is parabolic and the molecular distortion from the equilibrium position, where $\xi = 0$, always lies within the parabola. The quantised wavefunctions, $\theta_n(\xi)$, are seen to extend slightly outside the range of the parabolic curve. If more than two atoms are present the reduced mass has to be redefined and the change in bond length, x, has to be replaced by some other parameter.

25   Potential Energy and Bond Length

The harmonic approximation is good only for small displacements and a better approximation than equation (24.4) is due to Morse;

$$V = D[1 - \exp(-\beta x)]^2 \qquad (25.1)$$

where β is a constant and D is the molecular dissociation energy on the scale with zero energy at the equilibrium distance. In figure 25.1 the Morse curve is seen to give a fairly good agreement with the empirical potential energy curve derived from the optical spectrum of H_2; in other cases the agreement is less good.

The use of equation (25.1) in place of the harmonic approximation gives, in place of equation (24.9),

$$E_n = \frac{(n + \frac{1}{2})h\beta(2D/\mu)^{1/2}}{2\pi} - \frac{(n + \frac{1}{2})^2(h\beta)^2}{(2\pi)^2 2\mu}. \qquad (25.2)$$

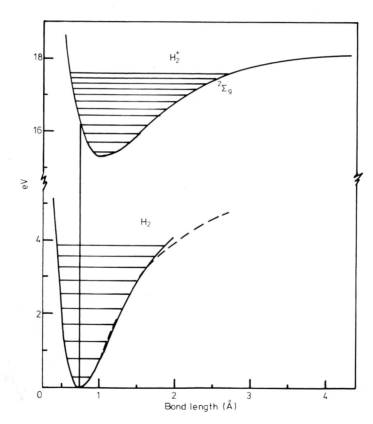

Figure 25.1. Potential curve of the H_2 and the H_2^+ electronic ground states with vibrational levels. The lower full curve is derived from the optical spectrum (Herzberg 1950), and the broken curve is that of the Morse equation. The upper curve was obtained from calculation (Lindholm 1972), and the vibrational levels were kindly supplied by J Berkowitz.

Various other potential functions and also elaboration of the Morse function have been suggested in order to give better agreement with the H_2 curve.

Comparison of equations (24.2) and (24.9) suggests the approximation

$$hv = \frac{h\beta(2D/\mu)^{1/2}}{2\pi}$$

(25.3)

so that equation (25.2) can be written

$$E_n = (n + \tfrac{1}{2})hv - (n + \tfrac{1}{2})^2 \frac{(hv)^2}{4D}.$$

(25.4)

Where a bending vibration is involved, the interval is often found to increase with n rather than to decrease, as implied by equation (25.4). This is a consequence of the increase in the force constant as atoms are brought into proximity by the bending.

26 The Franck–Condon Factor

The expression for the probability of absorption of a photon of light was given in § 7. If the molecule goes from the state of function ϕ to that symbolised by ϕ^+ during the transition, the probability will be proportional to the integral $\langle \phi | er | \phi^+ \rangle^2$. By invoking the Born–Oppenheimer principle, ϕ can be written $\psi\Theta$, where ψ is the

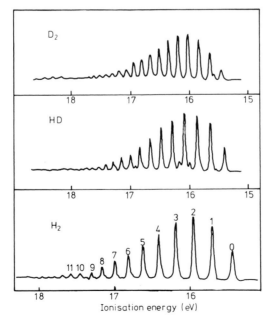

Figure 26.1. Photoelectron spectra of D_2, HD and H_2 obtained using He resonance radiation. The numbers in the H_2 spectrum denote the vibrational quantum number of the ionised state (Berkowitz and Spohr 1973).

Table 26.1. Ionisation energies, experimental intensities and calculated Franck–Condon factors for the ionisation of H_2, HD and D_2 (Berkowitz and Spohr 1973, Gardner and Samson 1976).

| Molecule | n(ion) | I(eV) | Experimental intensity | | Franck–Condon factor (Gardner and Samson 1976) |
			(Berkowitz and Spohr 1973)	(Gardner and Samson 1976)	
H_2	0	15·4254	0·463	0·448	0·521
	1	15·6971	0·863	0·918	0·918
	2	15·9530	1·000	1·000	1·000
	3	16·1936	0·884	0·969	0·879
	4	16·4194	0·700	0·713	0·689
	5	16·6308	0·579	0·572	0·508
	6	16·8281	0·472	0·423	0·361
	7	17·0113	0·313	0·308	0·253
	8	17·1808	0·241	0·208	0·176
	9	17·3365	0·137	0·132	0·122
	10	17·4783		0·089	0·085
	11	17·6061·		0·058	0·060
	12			0·039	0·042
	13			0·024	0·030
	14			0·015	0·021
	15			0·005	0·014
HD	0	15·444	0·300		0·402
	1	15·682	0·676		0·818
	2	15·907	1·000		1·000
	3	16·120	0·975		0·965
	4	16·329	0·963		0·816
	5	16·515	0·810		0·638
	6	16·710	0·634		0·475
	7	16·880	0·407		0·344
	8	17·040	0·264		0·245
	9	17·185	0·218		0·173
	10	17·330	0·160		0·123
D_2	0	15·466	0·230		0·260
	1	15·664	0·538		0·648
	2	15·854	0·812		0·940
	3	16·032	0·950		1·048
	4	16·206	1·000		1·000
	5	16·371	0·928		0·864
	6	16·528	0·756		0·699
	7	16·680	0·624		0·541
	8	16·824	0·487		0·407
	9	16·962	0·342		0·300
	10	17·087	0·270		0·219

electronic and Θ is the vibrational part of the total wavefunction. Because er is an electronic operator (r being an electronic position vector), it acts only upon the electronic part of the function,

$$\langle\phi|er|\phi^+\rangle = \langle\psi|er|\psi^+\rangle\langle\Theta|\Theta^+\rangle.$$

The square of the vibrational overlap integral, $\langle\Theta|\Theta^+\rangle^2$, is called the Franck–Condon factor. If there is a series of vibrational states associated with ψ^+, there will be a series of Franck–Condon factors, and the intensities of the corresponding vibrational peaks comprising the band in the photoelectron spectrum should be proportional to these Franck–Condon factors.

In accordance with the Franck–Condon principle the Franck–Condon overlap integrals are evaluated for the geometry of the neutral molecule in its initial state. In the ionised state, the equilibrium geometry is not necessarily the same; in hydrogen, for example, the bond length is 0·74 Å, but for the lowest state of H_2^+ it is 1·06 Å.

Experimental vibrational intensities of H_2, HD and D_2 (figure 26.1) are compared in table 26.1 with calculated Franck–Condon factors for the ionisation,

$$h\nu + H_2(^1\Sigma_g^+) \rightarrow {}^2\Sigma_g^+ + e^-.$$

Agreement is not exact but the most intense vibrational component is correctly predicted in two out of the three cases. Deficiencies arise from the neglect of rotations, the neglect of polarisation of the ion by the photoelectron, deviation of the neutral molecule from the equilibrium geometry caused by zero-point motion, and the failure of the Born–Oppenheimer principle.

27 Vibrational Interval

Vibrational structure arises from the formation of ions in different vibrational states, each state having its own characteristic energy, as shown in figure 25.1. At room temperature, most molecules are in the ground vibrational state and since the transition to the ionic state is 'vertical', as shown in figure 25.1, the resulting ionic state often has large vibrational amplitude, that is, it is a vibrationally excited state. The 'vertical' transition has the highest Franck–Condon factor.

Every state of a molecule has a characteristic dissociation energy; for example, the $^2\Sigma_g^+$ state of H_2^+ has $D = 2\cdot648$ eV. This value is the difference in energy between the horizontal part of the potential energy curve (where V becomes independent of r) and the minimum. D is also the maximum width (not always observed) of the vibrational progression of the corresponding band in the photo-electron spectrum.

The nth vibrational interval is the difference in energy between the $(n+1)$th and the nth vibrational peaks. This quantity, W_n, is plotted against n in figure 27.1 for H_2, HD and D_2. The dissociation energy is the area under the plot as long as the plot extends the full width of the band, that is, to the quantum number at which the vibrational interval becomes zero, but the plots in figure 27.1 do not extend that far. Only occasionally is the plot found to be linear, but where it is the dissociation energy is

$$D = \tfrac{1}{2} W_0 n_D$$

where W_0 is the first vibrational interval and n_D is the quantum number at which the interval becomes zero. Extrapolation of figure 27.1 gives the value $n_D = 19$ for H_2, although the last peak that can actually be seen in the spectrum is the eighteenth, at 18·08 eV (Lindholm 1972). A linear plot of W_n against n would

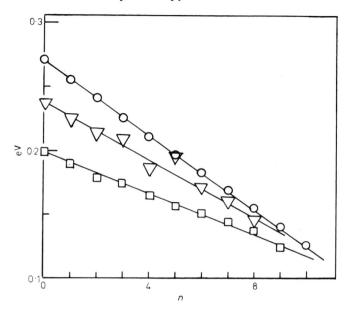

Figure 27.1. Plots of the vibrational interval against the vibrational quantum number, n, for the $^2\Sigma_g^+$ bands of H_2, HD and D_2. $\bigcirc$ H_2; $\triangledown$ HD; $\square$ D_2.

therefore imply

$$D = \tfrac{1}{2} \times 19 \times 0.2712$$

$$= 2.58 \text{ eV}.$$

The full width of the progression from $n = 0$ to $n = 18$ is observed to be 2.65 eV.

Vibrational frequency depends on the reduced mass (equation (25.3)), and the ratio of the vibrational intervals of H_2, HD and D_2 should be $1.41:1.22:1.00$. The observed ratios are $1.37:1.20:1.00$ for the first intervals (table 26.1).

That the energy of the 0–0 vibrational component is not the same for the three isotopes is a consequence of their different zero-point energies, that is, the values of E_n when $n = 0$ in equation (25.4). The lowest ionisation energy is called the *adiabatic* or *threshold* ionisation energy.

28   Vibrational Structure of Hydrogen Halide Spectra

The loss of an electron from the 1π orbital of a hydrogen halide molecule changes the dissociation energy only very slightly. In HBr, for example, the dissociation energy of the neutral molecule is 3.75 eV, whilst for the ion in its $1\pi^{-1}$ state the value is 3.89 eV. The reason for such a small change is the non-bonding nature of the orbital.

Further consequences are small changes in the equilibrium bond length and the vibrational function. The Franck–Condon factor is therefore to be evaluated with the same equilibrium bond length and vibrational function for both ion and molecule. The result is that only the 0–0 component possesses a large factor and it appears in the spectrum as a sharp peak split into components by spin–orbit interaction (figure 20.2). In HCl the 0–1 component has about one twentieth of the intensity of the 0–0 component and can be picked out under good resolution (Delwiche *et al* 1973), but further members are missing.

When the photoelectron comes from a bonding molecular orbital, on the other hand, the equilibrium bond length increases; the vertical and most favourable overlap is then for a higher member than the 0–0 component. A good example is the hydrogen molecule (figure 25.1), where the Franck–Condon factor is appreciable for a number of components and a series of vibrational peaks is observed. Ionisation of the $3\sigma^+$ orbitals of the hydrogen halides produces bands of this type, although there are complications caused by dissociation of the molecule; about half-way through the bands of HCl and HBr the structure is lost and they become continua (figure 28.1), whilst the bands of HF and HI are continua throughout.

Consideration of the dissociation energy of HBr (3·75 eV) enables a discrimination to be made between the alternative dissociations

$$HBr^+ \rightarrow H + Br^+ \tag{28.1}$$

and

$$HBr^+ \rightarrow H^+ + Br. \tag{28.2}$$

The dissociation energies of the above are

$$D(HBr) = 3\cdot75 + I$$

where I is the ionisation energy of Br in equation (28.1) and of H in equation (28.2); 11·84 eV and 13·6 eV, respectively. Hence the dissociation giving Br^+ requires 15·59 eV and that giving H^+ requires 17·35 eV. Since dissociation in fact sets in below 16 eV it is clear that Br^+ is the product. A plot of vibrational interval against vibrational quantum number after the fashion of figure 27.1 has a negative slope up to the 0–3 component at about 15·8 eV, but it then breaks off and becomes positive. This suggests something like a Morse potential up to $n = 3$, followed by a curve of a different sort due to the mixing of the $^2\Sigma^+$ state with another of repulsive nature.

An idea of the nature of the repulsive state of HBr^+ can be gained from Ehrenfest's *adiabatic principle*. According to this principle, the value of any quantum number characterising a conjunction of two systems is what it would be if the two were somehow insulated from each other so that there was no interaction of any kind, brought together from infinite separation and then allowed slowly to interact by removing the insulation.

Consider the dissociation of a diatomic molecule under these conditions. The molecular states are characterised by a quantum number, m, for angular momentum about the axis. With reference to this axis, the atomic angular momentum components are M_1 and M_2 and their resultant is conserved under the adiabatic conditions

$$m = M_1 + M_2. \tag{28.3}$$

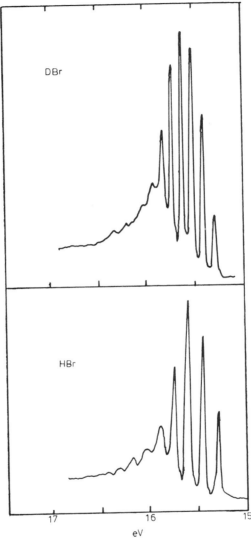

Figure 28.1. The photoelectron spectra of HBr and DBr for the ionisation of the $3\sigma^{+}$ orbital. Dissociation takes place at 15·6 eV. Spectra obtained with He(I) radiation (Delwiche *et al* 1973).

For example, a P and an S state having

$$M_1 = \pm 1, 0$$

$$M_2 = 0$$

give three possible values for m, namely, ± 1, 0. No distinction is made between the opposite signs in a diatomic molecule, as states which differ only in sign are degenerate and merely involve opposite senses of rotation. Hence equation (28.3) could have been written

$$m = |M_1 + M_2| \qquad (28.4)$$

and we have a Π and a Σ state. Note that states with $m = 0$, 1, 2, 3, etc, are symbolised Σ, Π, Δ, Φ, etc, in analogy with atomic nomenclature.

The dissociation of HBr^+ into $H + Br^+$ gives a ^2S state for H and a p^4 configuration for Br^+, which implies (table 10.2) either ^1S, ^1D or ^3P. Of the latter, ^3P lies lowest in energy and it is therefore necessary to consider the states of HBr^+ relating to $H(^2S)$ and $Br^+(^3P)$.

The total spin quantum number of the molecule takes the values

$$S = (S_1 + S_2), \qquad (S_1 + S_2 - 1), \qquad (S_1 + S_2 - 2), \ldots, (S_1 - S_2); \qquad (28.5)$$

hence ^2S and ^3P arise from the quartet and doublet states $^{2,4}(\Sigma, \Pi)$.

It remains to be decided whether the Σ states are Σ^+ or Σ^- (table 23.1). The *parity* of the atomic states is important here. In general, atomic states are either odd (umgerade, denoted u) or even (gerade, denoted g), depending on their eigenfunctions with respect to the parity operator, $\hat{P}$. $\hat{P}$ converts x, y and z into $-x$, $-y$ and $-z$, so that these are of u type. The one-electron atomic function $\phi(n, l, m)$ is converted into $(-1)^l \phi(n, l, m)$, and for the polyelectronic function,

$$\hat{P}\psi = (-1)^{\Sigma l}\psi$$

where ψ is given by equation (8.3). According to a rule due to Wigner and Witmer

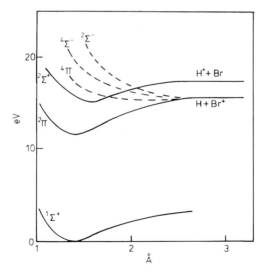

Figure 28.2. Potential energy curves of HBr (Lempka *et al* 1968). The $^2\Sigma^+$ state formed by the ionisation of the $3\sigma^+$ orbital is stable, but where it crosses the repulsive curves the ion passes into the corresponding repulsive state and dissociation takes place.

we have Σ^- when the sum

$$L_1 + L_2 + \Sigma l_1 + \Sigma l_2$$

is odd, and Σ^+ when the sum is even. In our case,

$$^1S(s^1), \qquad L = 0, \qquad \Sigma l = 0$$

$$^3P(p^4), \qquad L = 1, \qquad \Sigma l = 4$$

the sum is odd and we have Σ^-. Hence the possible states dissociating to $H + Br^+$ with the lowest energy are $^{2,4}(\Sigma^-, \Pi)$. Absent from among these states is $^2\Sigma^+$, which results from the loss of the $3\sigma^+$ electron; a transition to one of the other states must therefore occur before dissociation.

The quartet states of HBr are unstable because their extra electronic spin can be acquired only at the expense of promoting an electron to an antibonding orbital. Similarly, the Σ^- states require the promotion of 1π electrons (two π electrons give Σ^+, Σ^- and Δ symmetry) and only the $^2\Pi$ state is stable (figure 28.2).

For HI the dissociation energies are calculated to be $13 \cdot 49$ eV for the formation of $H + I^+$ and $16 \cdot 65$ eV for $H^+ + I$. The entire 3σ band lies within the dissociation continuum and there is no vibrational structure.

In HCl the dissociation energies are calculated to be $17 \cdot 44$ eV ($H + Cl^+$) and $18 \cdot 03$ eV ($H^+ + Cl$), and a decrease in the intensity of the vibrational structure is found after the 0–4 vibrational peak at about $17 \cdot 1$ eV (Lempka *et al* 1968). In HF the lowest dissociation energy is found for $H^+ + F$ at $19 \cdot 41$ eV, and no vibrational structure is observed.

29   Hydrogen Cyanide

The vibrational structure of a photoelectron spectrum is greatly simplified by the fact that the only modes to appear are those which involve distortions of those bonds whose strength depends on the orbital being ionised. This follows from the considerations of the last section where it was shown that unless the loss of the photoelectron changes the potential energy curve, only the 0–0 vibrational component has appreciable intensity.

In HCN both the 1π and the $5\sigma^+$ orbitals are C—N bonding (figure 29.1), and progressions of C—N stretching vibrations are found in the corresponding bands.

Table 29.1. HCN: the results of an *ab initio* calculation of energy eigenvalues (von Niessen *et al* 1976) and ionisation potentials corrected for relaxation and correlation effects.

Orbital	Energy eigenvalue (eV)	Ionisation energy (eV)
$1\sigma^+$	$-424 \cdot 6$	
$2\sigma^+$	$-307 \cdot 39$	
$3\sigma^+$	$-33 \cdot 77$	
$4\sigma^+$	$-22 \cdot 13$	$20 \cdot 49$
$5\sigma^+$	$-15 \cdot 85$	$13 \cdot 92$
1π	$-13 \cdot 65$	$13 \cdot 50$

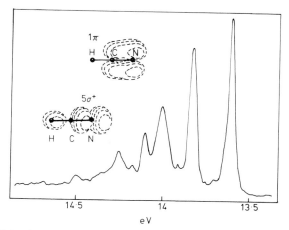

Figure 29.1. Photoelectron spectrum of HCN (Frost *et al* 1973b) showing the region of lowest ionisation energy. There are two molecular orbitals being ionised in this region; 1π and $5\sigma^+$. Both orbitals are C–N bonding and the complex vibrational pattern contains progressions of C–N stretching vibrations.

The ionisation energies of 1π and $5\sigma^+$ are calculated to be only 0.42 eV apart (table 29.1) and therefore both bands are present in figure 29.1. The pattern of vibrational peaks is complex but the C—N vibrational interval is picked out at 0.223 eV (1800 cm^{-1}), compared with 0.259 eV (2097 cm^{-1}) in the neutral molecule. The vibration concerned is ν_3 shown in figure 29.2(c); its decrease in energy

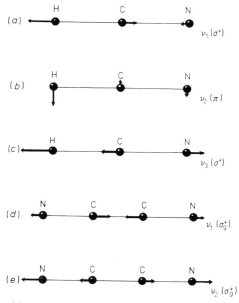

Figure 29.2. (*a*) – (*c*) Normal modes of vibration for HCN; (*d*) and (*e*) cyanogen.

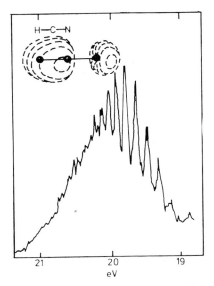

Figure 29.3. Photoelectron spectrum of HCN showing the ionisation of the $4\sigma^+$ orbital (Baker and Turner 1968). There is a progression of C—H stretching vibrations which terminates at a dissociation continuum.

upon ionisation follows from the loss of chemical bonding. Ionisation of an anti-bonding orbital produces the opposite change, an instance being Cl_2, where the lowest ionisation is associated with a vibrational interval of 0·08 eV, as compared with 0·07 eV from the IR spectrum (Evans and Orchard 1971).

The $4\sigma^+$ orbital is C—H bonding (figure 29.3), and there is a progression of C—H (ν_1) vibrations which break off at about 20 eV (figure 29.2(*a*)). There is a very large reduction in the ν_1 vibrational frequency; it falls from 0·411 eV (3311 cm^{-1}) in the neutral molecule to 0·209 eV (1690 cm^{-1}). The breaking off is in accordance with the dissociation

$$HCN^+ \rightarrow H + CN^+$$

where the energy is $D(H—CN) + I(CN) = 4·8 + 15·3 = 20·1$ eV. The dissociation results in a lowering of the centroid of the band because the part of it lying above 20 eV is weakened. This explains the discrepancy between the calculated and the observed vertical ionisation energies (table 29.1).

30 Linear Conjugated Molecules

The series consisting of acetylene (HC≡CH), diacetylene (HC≡C—C≡CH) and triacetylene (HC≡C—C≡C—C≡CH) is isoelectronic with the series hydrogen cyanide (HC≡N), cyanogen (N≡C—C≡N) and dicyanoacetylene (N≡C—C≡C—C≡N). There is an overall similarity between the spectra of HCN and acetylene (figures 29.1, 29.3 and 30.1).

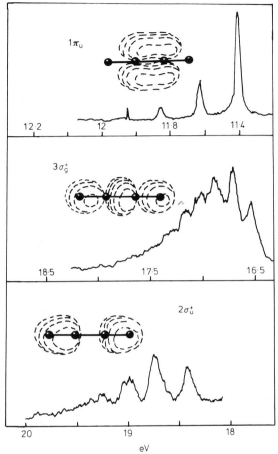

Figure 30.1. The photoelectron spectrum of acetylene (Baker and Turner 1968). The middle spectrum is that of the deuterated compound in which the vibrational structure is clearer.

For a molecule of $D_{\infty h}$ symmetry, the conjugated electrons are in orbitals similar to those of a free electron and run the length, L, of the molecule, the wavefunctions being

$$\Omega_n = (2/L)^{1/2} \sin(n\pi x/L) \tag{30.1}$$

where x is the distance of the electron from one end of the molecule. The quantum number n takes the values 1, 2, 3, etc, and these functions are zero when $x = 0$ or L, also the electron is confined to the length of the molecule. The wavelength (figure 30.2) is

$$\lambda_n = 2L/n$$

and de Broglie's relation gives for the energy

$$E_n = (nh)^2/(8mL^2). \tag{30.2}$$

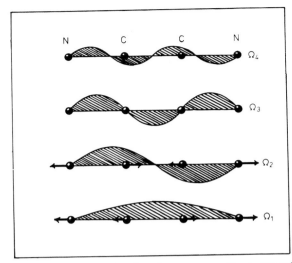

Figure 30.2. Free-electron wavefunctions for cyanogen. The lower pair only are occupied, and the vibrational modes excited by their ionisation are indicated by arrows.

The upper occupied orbital of acetylene ($1\pi_u$ in figure 30.1) takes the value $n = 1$; the central bond possesses the greater part of the electronic density and ionisation produces a progression of ν_2 vibrations (figure 29.2(e)). The vibrational separation is $0{\cdot}2268$ eV (1830 cm^{-1}), compared with $0{\cdot}2458$ eV (1983 cm^{-1}) in the neutral molecule.

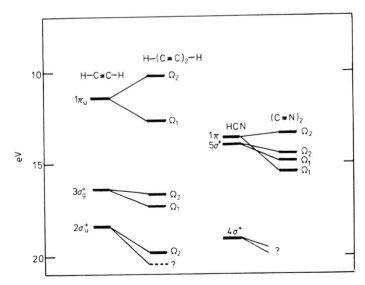

Figure 30.3. Molecular orbital energy diagram showing the observed ionisation energies. The orbitals of diacetylene are correlated with those of acetylene: similarly, the orbitals of HCN are correlated with those of cyanogen.

In diacetylene and cyanogen the uppermost occupied orbital is Ω_2 (figure 30.3), and in the case of cyanogen the expected vibrational progression involves $C\equiv N$ rather than $C\equiv C$ stretching. Accordingly, ν_1 (figure 29.2) vibrations are prominent in the first band and ν_2 vibrations are found in the band corresponding to the ionisation of Ω_1.

In triacetylene and dicyanoacetylene the uppermost occupied orbital is Ω_3 and the vibrational structure is complex in the associated band.

31 Changes in Bond Length and Angle on Ionisation

Suppose that the shape of a particular band in a photoelectron spectrum is due to a particular vibrational progression. It is possible to calculate the change in bond length on ionisation knowing the frequency of the vibration and the energies of onset and maximum intensity of the band, I_a and I_v, respectively. Assuming the potential energy to be $\frac{1}{2}kQ^2$ (equation (24.4)), where Q is some normal mode parameter such as a bond length, equation (24.6) gives

$$Q = \frac{1}{\pi\nu}\left(\frac{V}{2\mu}\right)^{1/2}. \tag{31.1}$$

The potential energy difference between the ionic and the neutral state is $I_v - I_a$ (figure 31.1), hence

$$\Delta Q = \frac{1}{\pi\nu}\left[\frac{(I_v - I_a)}{2\mu}\right]^{1/2}. \tag{31.2}$$

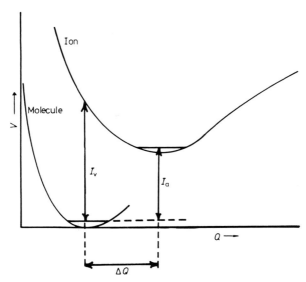

Figure 31.1. Potential energy curves of ion and molecule showing the relationship between the threshold ionisation energy, I_a, and the ionisation energy of maximum intensity, I_v (a and v denote adiabatic and vertical, respectively). The change of the coordinate on ionisation, ΔQ, is given by equation (31.2).

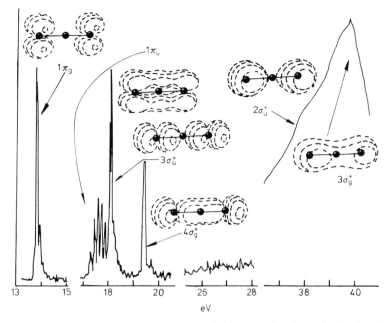

Figure 31.2. The photoelectron spectrum of CO_2 (gas phase) obtained using He resonance radiation (Gardner and Samson 1973).

Often v is measured in cm^{-1}, I in eV and μ in units of proton masses; equation (31.2) is then

$$\Delta Q(\text{Å}) = \frac{734}{v} \left[\frac{(I_v - I_a)}{\mu} \right]^{1/2}.$$

The change in bond length on ionisation of hydrogen can be calculated from the data in table 26.1. Taking I_v as the energy of the peak with the greatest Franck–Condon factor, the increments found are 0·35 Å (H_2), 0·33 Å (HD) and 0·37 Å (D_2). The bond length of H_2 in the neutral condition is 0·742 Å, and therefore that of $H_2^+(^2\Sigma_g^+)$ is about 1·09 Å. Analysis of the optical spectrum of H_2 gives the value 0·32 Å for the increase in bond length (Herzberg 1950).

In the spectrum of carbon dioxide (figure 31.2), the second band possesses a well resolved vibrational structure. The orbital being ionised is $1\pi_u$ and symmetrical stretching vibrations are anticipated, that is, vibrations in which the central atom is motionless and the oxygen atoms vibrate as in a diatomic molecule. Equation (31.2) is directly applicable but ΔQ is twice the change in the C—O bond length. Taking $I_a = 17\cdot32$ eV and $I_v = 17\cdot59$ eV, with $n = 2$ for the vibrational peak of the highest intensity, we obtain the value 0·062 Å for the increment in the C—O bond length. Analysis of the optical spectrum gives the result 0·0662 Å (Herzberg 1966); in the neutral molecule the bond length is 1·162 Å.

Ionisation of the $3a_1$ orbital of water weakens the force holding the molecule in nonlinear geometry (§§ 17 and 21). In the spectrum there is a well resolved progression of ν_2' bending vibrations (figure 23.1). If L is the bond length and θ is the H—O—H angle,

$$V = \tfrac{1}{2}k(L\theta)^2.$$

Clearly, ΔQ in equation (31.2) becomes $L\Delta\theta$ in this case. Taking the values $L = 0\cdot958$ Å, $I_a = 13\cdot78$ eV, $I_v = 14\cdot74$ eV and $\nu = 887\,\mathrm{cm}^{-1}$ (Potts and Price 1972), we find $\theta = 68°$.

This calculation has errors inherent in the harmonic approximation and perhaps all that can be concluded is that the angle is much closer to $180°$ in the ion than it is in the neutral molecule, where the value is $104°\ 27'$, but the Walsh diagram (figure 21.1) is thus confirmed.

32 Vibrational Inversion

If the amplitude is great enough the ν_2' vibration of water inverts the molecule through its centre of mass, turning it 'inside out'; this is called vibrational inversion. Where an inversion mode is present the potential energy curve obviously has two identical minima.

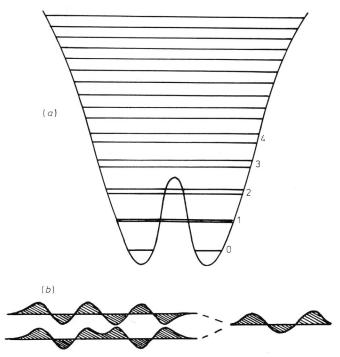

Figure 32.1. (a) Potential energy curve in the presence of an inversion mode of vibration. (b) On the right-hand side is drawn the $n = 2$ vibrational mode, and on the left-hand side a pair of the same modes have interacted in-phase and out-of-phase. Interaction takes place near and above the central barrier to inversion.

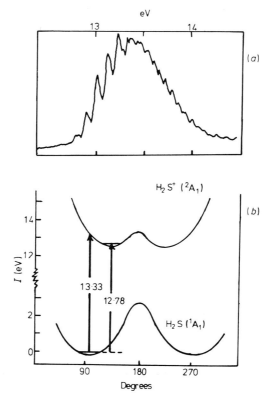

Figure 32.2. (*a*) The photoelectron spectrum of H_2S in the region of ionisation of the $3a_1$ electronic orbital (cf figure 17.2). The inversion barrier is surmounted at 13·3 eV, where a halving of the vibrational interval is seen (Potts and Price 1972). (*b*) Schematic potential energy plot of the ground state of H_2S and the $3a_1^{-1}$ state of H_2S^+. The adiabatic and vertical ionisation energies are shown.

At the bottom of the potential energy well in figure 32.1(*a*) where the two geometries are separate, there is no interaction between them. At higher energies, where the amplitude is so great that the molecule passes from one geometry to another during a vibrational cycle, interaction between the vibrational wavefunctions does take place. Where there is no interaction the pairs of functions are identical and degenerate. Interaction takes the form of in-phase and out-of-phase mixing, as illustrated in figure 32.1(*b*), with the result that every pair produces two non-degenerate resultants. When the central barrier to inversion is surmounted the number of vibrational intervals in the progression is doubled and the interval between them is halved.

Such a change is clearly seen at 13·3 eV in the $3a_1$ peak of H_2S in figure 32.2(*a*), where the progression of ν_2' vibrations suffers a decrease in interval from 910 to 540 cm^{-1}. It is concluded that the ion becomes linear at 13·3 eV. The onset of the band occurs at 12·78 eV and, assuming that this is the 0–0 energy, the height of the barrier to inversion is 0·52 eV.

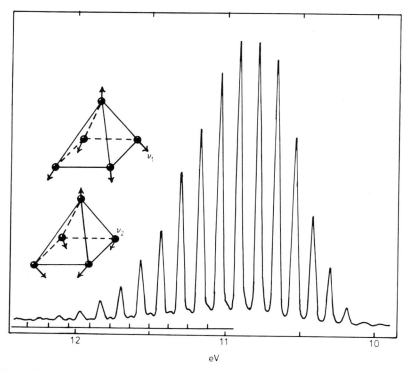

Figure 32.3. The photoelectron spectrum of ammonia in the region of ionisation of the $3a_1$ band (cf figure 17.2) showing two progressions of the inversion mode, ν_2. The weaker of the two progressions is picked out by the vertical bars at the lower left of the figure; this probably arises from one quantum of ν_1 plus the ν_2 quanta (Rabalais *et al* 1972).

In water the ion resulting from the ionisation of $3a_1$ is linear throughout the band; the vibrational interval is $887\ \mathrm{cm}^{-1}$ in the band as opposed to $1595\ \mathrm{cm}^{-1}$ in the neutral molecule. In H_2Se and H_2Te the vibrational structure is more diffuse, possibly on account of dissociation, but the situation seems to resemble that in H_2S (Potts and Price 1972).

In ammonia the loss of an electron from the $3a_1$ orbital loosens the constraint preventing the molecule from becoming planar. The vibrational mode seen in the spectrum is therefore the ν_2 or 'umbrella mode' (so called because the inversion of ammonia reminds one of an umbrella being blown inside out in the wind; see figure 32.3). The method of § 31 gives a planar geometry both for ammonia and its heavier congeners. From the IR spectrum the vibrational frequencies (in cm^{-1}) are 950 (NH_3), 992 (PH_3), 906 (AsH_3) and 781 (SbH_3), whereas the vibrational intervals in the photoelectron spectrum (in cm^{-1}) are 900 (NH_3), 489 (PH_3), 452 (AsH_3) and 387 (SbH_3).

The reduction by a factor of two in the above series is in agreement with the foregoing, although ammonia itself is anomalous. The vibration in ammonia is in fact complicated by a number of factors: the barrier to inversion is low ($0\cdot25\ \mathrm{eV}$), and there is interaction between ν_1 and ν_2 vibrations (figure 32.3). The ν_2 interval in the $3a_1$ progression of ammonia increases with n from 896 cm^{-1} to 1130 cm^{-1}, in the opposite direction from that predicted by the Morse equation. There are two progressions in the $3a_1$ band of ammonia, the weaker of the two being intervals of ν_2 plus one quantum of ν_1 with a frequency of 2743 cm^{-1}. In the IR spectrum the frequency of ν_1 is 3337 cm^{-1}.

33   The Jahn–Teller Effect

Vibrations other than totally symmetric ones can alter the symmetry of a molecule. This sometimes has the effect that the degeneracy of a certain irreducible representation is raised; a splitting into two or more occurs. When this happens we say that the symmetry has been lowered. For example, in figure 21.1 we see that in the linear geometry the $1b_1$ and $3a_1$ orbitals of H_2O are degenerate, being the $1\pi_u$ orbitals of $D_{\infty h}$. Hence we could say that for water in the linear configuration, bending vibrations raise the degeneracy of $1\pi_u$. The *static Jahn–Teller* effect states that in certain instances the lower symmetry has the lower energy so that the equilibrium geometry is the one of lower symmetry. In photoelectron spectroscopy the *dynamic Jahn–Teller* effect is encountered as the splitting of a band into two or more components. This arises when the degeneracy of the orbital being ionised is susceptible to being raised by vibrations even though the equilibrium geometry is that of the higher symmetry.

The equilibrium geometry of a molecule is only an average about which the molecule fluctuates, and the geometry in which the molecule finds itself at the

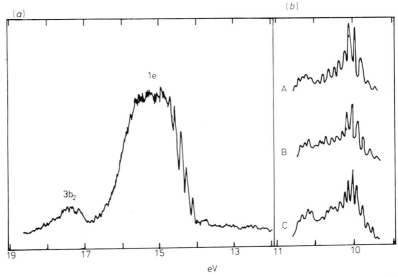

Figure 33.1. The photoelectron spectrum of allene. (*a*) The second and third bands (Turner *et al* 1970). (*b*) The first bands of allene (curve A); allene-1,1-D_2 (curve B), and allene-D_4 (curve C) (Thomas and Thompson 1974). The first bands show evidence of the dynamic Jahn–Teller effect as there are two humps at 10·0 and 10·6 eV.

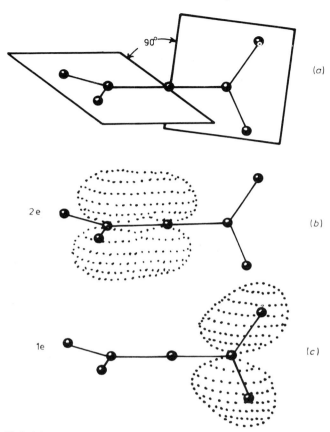

Figure 33.2. (*a*) The equilibrium geometry of allene. The C–C–C assembly is linear and the dihedral angle, θ, between the planes defined by the CH$_2$ groups is 90°. The point group is D$_{2d}$, and the x axis lies perpendicular to the C–C–C axis and bisects the dihedral angle. (*b*) and (*c*) Lobes of the molecular orbitals of e symmetry.

instant when the photoelectric effect occurs is not always that of equilibrium. Subsequently, the ion relaxes to its new geometry from the 'Franck–Condon geometry', as it is sometimes called. This relaxation may possibly involve the static Jahn–Teller effect, but the dynamic effect does not depend upon relaxation at all; the important point is that in the Franck–Condon geometry the degeneracies of the molecule are already raised. How great an effect this has upon the photoelectron spectrum depends upon the susceptibility of the orbitals to vibrational distortion. In allene, for example, the 2e orbital is much more susceptible than is the 1e orbital (figures 33.1 and 33.2).

Allene is CH$_2$=C=CH$_2$ and the point group is D$_{2d}$ (table 33.1). The first band in the spectrum results from the ionisation of the C=C bonding π orbital labelled 2e, and the second band belongs to the 1e orbital.

In the neutral molecule the dihedral angle, θ, between the planes defined by the CH$_2$ groups is a right angle. There are two potentially Jahn–Teller-active vibra-

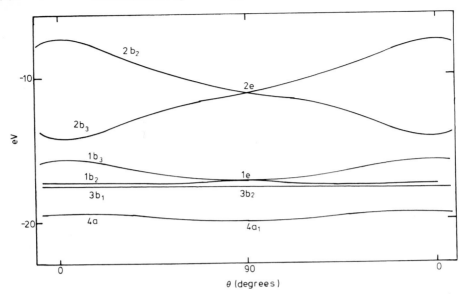

Figure 33.3. Walsh diagram for allene. The dihedral angle, θ, is defined in figure 33.2 (Buenker and Peyerimhoff 1974).

tions: asymmetrical stretching along the C–C–C axis (b_2 stretch), and the torsional mode in which the dihedral angle oscillates (b_1). b_2 stretch lowers the symmetry to C_{2v} and the torsional mode lowers it to D_2 (except when $\theta = 0$, which gives D_{2h}). In table 33.2 is shown the correlation between the symmetry species when the symmetry is lowered.

Table 33.1. Character table for D_{2d}.

	E	$2S_4$	$C_2(z)$	$2C_2'$	$2\sigma_d$	
A_1	1	1	1	1	1	$x^2+y^2,\ z^2$
A_2	1	1	1	-1	-1	R_z
B_1	1	-1	1	1	-1	x^2-y^2
B_2	1	-1	1	-1	1	$z,\ xy$
E	2	0	-2	0	0	$x,\ y,\ R_x,\ R_y,$ $xz,\ yz.$

Table 33.2. Correlation between irreducible representations of D_{2d}, D_2 and C_{2v}.

D_{2d}	D_2	C_{2v}
A_1	a	a_1
A_2	b_1	a_2
B_1	a	a_2
B_2	b_1	a_1
E	b_2+b_3	b_1+b_2

The Jahn–Teller effect causes a double humping of the first band of allene and an erratic vibrational spacing. There is a rapid decrease in the vibrational interval, the first being 807 cm^{-1} and the twelfth being exactly half of this. In the IR spectrum of allene there is a torsional mode at 865 cm^{-1}, and the discussion is continued with the assumption that this mode is responsible for the Jahn–Teller effect in allene.

Figure 33.3 is the Walsh diagram for allene, where the molecular parameter is θ. From the separation of the two humps in the spectrum, the Jahn–Teller splitting is estimated to be about 0·6 eV. Inspection of the Walsh diagram indicates that the dihedral angle has to differ from the equilibrium value by about 12° in order to produce a splitting of this size. We can take 12° to be the average distortion of the Franck–Condon state. Inspection of the Walsh diagram indicates that the loss of a 2e electron (alternatively, a $2b_2$ electron in the lower symmetry) would destabilise the geometry of the neutral molecule. Calculations indicate that $\theta = 38°$ in the $2e^{-1}$ ion at equilibrium (Haselbach 1970).

The second band in the spectrum lacks the two humps of the first. Reference to the Walsh diagram indicates that a 12° displacement of the dihedral angle from the equilibrium angle would result in a splitting of only 0·1 eV, which would be unresolved in the spectrum.

34   Jahn–Teller-Active Vibrations

When the electronic eigenfunction is sensitive to the vibrational coordinate, the Born–Oppenheimer principle loses its validity. Such a situation is usually encountered only at or near degeneracy, but the Franck–Condon principle is unaffected. Suppose that H_0 is the Hamiltonian for the degenerate configuration and its eigenfunctions are ψ_i. $\langle \psi_i | H_0 | \psi_j \rangle = E_0$ if $i = j$, otherwise the value is zero. The effect of the vibration with the displacement vector $\boldsymbol{Q}$ can be taken into account by writing the Hamiltonian as a power series in $\boldsymbol{Q}$:

$$H = H_0 + V'\boldsymbol{Q} + V''\boldsymbol{Q}^2 + \ldots \tag{34.1}$$

The terms in $\boldsymbol{Q}$ lead to the mixing of the original wavefunctions to give new ones:

$$\xi_i = \sum_i c_i \psi_i. \tag{34.2}$$

This equation is analogous to (18.1) and the energies of the new functions are obtained from equation (18.4). Neglecting terms above the first order in $\boldsymbol{Q}$ we have, for example, in the doubly degenerate case,

$$\begin{vmatrix} (H_0 - E) & V'\boldsymbol{Q} \\ V'\boldsymbol{Q} & (H_0 - E) \end{vmatrix} = 0$$

with the solutions,

$$E = E_0 \pm \langle \psi_1 | V'\boldsymbol{Q} | \psi_2 \rangle. \tag{34.3}$$

The original functions remain degenerate in energy unless the off-diagonal element, $\langle \psi_1 | V'\boldsymbol{Q} | \psi_2 \rangle$, is finite. This condition is fulfilled only if the element is

Table 34.1. Direct products for the point group D_{2d}.

	A_1	A_2	B_1	B_2	E
A_1	A_1	A_2	B_1	B_2	E
A_2		A_1	B_2	B_1	E
B_1			A_1	A_2	E
B_2				A_1	E
E					A_1, A_2, B_1, B_2

symmetric, that is, only if Q transforms as one of the representations spanned by the basis $\psi_1 \times \psi_2$. In general, the direct product of ψ_i and ψ_j must contain a component of the same irreducible representation as Q (see Appendix IV).

Returning to the example of allene discussed in § 33, it can be seen from table 34.1 that the direct product $e \times e$ gives $a_1 + a_2 + b_1 + b_2$ in the point group D_{2d}. In order that a vibration be Jahn–Teller-active it must therefore be of either b_1 or b_2 symmetry (a_2 is of rotational symmetry).

35   The Jahn–Teller Effect in Cyclopropane

Cyclopropane, $(CH_2)_3$, is a gas which boils at $-34\,°C$. The point group is D_{3h} and the degenerate representations are e' and e'' (table 35.1). Both of these have the self-product $a'_1 + a'_2 + e'$, and only vibrations of e' symmetry are Jahn–Teller-active according to the first-order approximation of § 34. The geometry of cyclopropane is

Table 35.1. Character table for the point group D_{3h}.

D_{3h}	E	$2C_3(z)$	$3C'_2$	$\sigma_h(xy)$	$2S_3$	$3\sigma_v$	
A'_1	1	1	1	1	1	1	x^2+y^2, z^2
A'_2	1	1	-1	1	1	-1	R_z
E'	2	-1	0	2	-1	0	x, y, x^2-y^2, xy
A''_1	1	1	1	-1	-1	-1	
A''_2	1	1	-1	-1	-1	1	z
E''	2	-1	0	-2	1	0	R_x, R_y, xz, yz

illustrated in figure 35.1 and the molecular distortion resulting from a vibration of e' symmetry is suggested in figure 35.2. The e' vibrations can be regarded either as oscillations along x and y (which lie in the plane of the carbon atoms) or, alternatively, as a displacement rotating about the C_3 axis, which can be expressed in terms of an amplitude, q, and an angle, ϕ,

$$x = q \cos \phi$$

$$y = q \sin \phi$$

$$x + iy = q \exp(\pm i\phi). \tag{35.1}$$

The vibrations can be regarded as clockwise and anticlockwise rotational displacements to which the angular momentum quantum number, l, can be assigned so that we have $\exp(\pm il\phi)$. Pairs having the same value of l are degenerate.

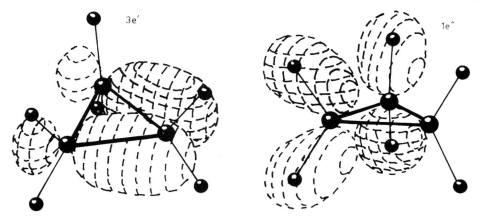

Figure 35.1. The upper occupied orbitals of cyclopropane. Doubly hatched lobes are of the opposite sign to those that are singly hatched.

The electronic density contours of the 3e' and the 1e" orbitals are depicted in figure 35.1; the latter has a nodal plane coincident with the plane of the carbon atoms. The 3e' band of the spectrum possesses a pronounced Jahn–Teller splitting (figure 35.3), but there is none visible in the 1e" band. It is not surprising that this should be the case having regard to the orbital density contours; 1e" is C—H bonding, 3e' is C—C bonding and the e' vibrations, being in-plane, affect the C—C bonds the most. The Walsh diagram in figure 35.3 confirms this supposition.

The observed magnitude of the Jahn–Teller splitting of the first band in the spectrum is 0·77 eV, and a vibrational distortion of the C–C–C angle of about 4° is

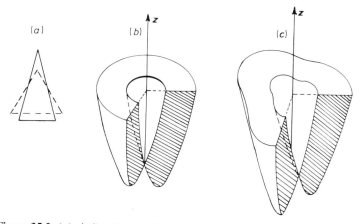

Figure 35.2. (*a*) e' vibrations produce the maximum Jahn–Teller splitting for the distortion from equilateral to isosceles geometry. (*b*) The axially symmetric energy surfaces obtained with equation (34.3) with the addition of a term for the Hooke's law energy, $\frac{1}{2}kQ^2$. Two surfaces are seen to become degenerate at the z axis. (*c*) Potential energy surfaces of trigonal symmetry obtained from equation (35.4) (Longuet-Higgins 1961).

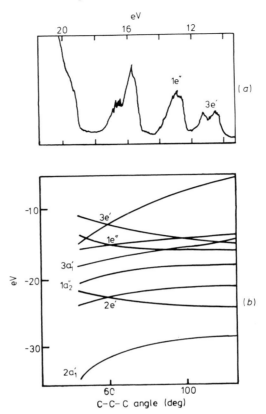

Figure 35.3. (*a*) The photoelectron spectrum of cyclopropane (gas phase) at 20·21 eV (Basch *et al* 1969). (*b*) Walsh diagram for cyclopropane (Buenker and Peyerimhoff 1974). The energy eigenvalues of the orbitals are plotted against the C–C–C angle.

indicated from the curve for 3e′ in the Walsh diagram. Corresponding to a 4° distortion, the splitting of the 1e″ band can be estimated to be at about 0·4 eV: this is not evident in the spectrum although the shape of the band suggests that two peaks are present but not separated.

   Allowing q_+ and q_- to represent in equation (35.1) the clockwise and the anticlockwise displacement vectors of the vibrations and substituting them in equation (34.1), whilst retaining only the linear and quadratic terms,

$$H = H_0 + V'(q_+ + q_-) + V''(q_+ + q_-)^2$$
$$= H_0 + V'q_+ + V'q_- + V''q_+^2 + V''q_-^2 + 2V''q_+q_-. \qquad (35.2)$$

Some of the above terms lead to zero matrix elements. In order to show this, it is convenient to write the degenerate electronic wavefunctions in the form

$$\psi_\pm = \psi \exp(\pm i\phi). \qquad (35.3)$$

The diagonal matrix elements are now $\langle\psi_+|H|\psi_+\rangle = \langle\psi_-|H|\psi_-\rangle$ and the off-diagonal elements are $\langle\psi_+|H|\psi_-\rangle = \langle\psi_-|H|\psi_+\rangle$.

The matrix elements have the units of energy, they are unchanged by any symmetry transformation, and must therefore be totally symmetric. Only those terms of equation (35.2) give nonzero elements that have the same symmetry as ψ_+^2 for the diagonal matrix elements, and the same as $\psi_+\psi_-$ for the off-diagonal elements.

Since $\psi_+^2 = \psi^2$ (remembering to multiply by the complex conjugate of equation (35.3)), it has no angular dependence and only those terms of equation (35.2) that are similarly independent yield a finite matrix element, namely, $H_0 + 2V''q_+q_-$. Since

$$\psi_+\psi_- = \psi^2 \exp(2i\phi),$$

the retained terms of equation (35.2) for this off-diagonal element are $V''q_+^2 + V'q_-$. That the latter terms transform identically under the C_3 operation is evident since

$$\hat{C}_3 q_+^2 = \exp[i(4\pi/3)]q_+^2$$
$$= \exp[i(-2\pi/3)]q_+^2$$
$$\hat{C}_3 q_- = \exp[i(-2\pi/3)]q_-.$$

The determinant is now

$$\begin{vmatrix} (H_0 + 2V''q_+q_- - E) & (V'q_- + V''q_+^2) \\ (V'q_+ + V''q_-^2) & (H_0 + 2V''q_+q_- - E) \end{vmatrix} = 0$$

and the solution is

$$E = E_0 + 2V''q^2 \pm [(V'q)^2 + (V''q^2)^2 + 2V'V''q^3 \cos 3\phi]^{1/2}$$
$$\simeq E_0 + 2V''q^2 \pm (V'q + V''q^2 \cos 3\phi). \tag{35.4}$$

The above is correct to the third order in q.

The quadratic term, $2V''q^2$, can be identified with the Hooke's law energy, and $\pm V'q$ is evidently the same as in equation (34.3). The term in $\cos 3\phi$ has the effect of putting three minima into the potential energy curve (figure 35.2) at points $120°$ apart. The Jahn–Teller splitting is maximal when the molecular geometry is at one of these minima; such a geometry is exemplified by figure 35.2(*a*).

Problems

1 Show that the vibrations of NH_3 are of a_1 and e symmetry (use table 22.1 and equation (22.1)). The frequencies observed in the infrared are $3335\cdot9$ and $3337\cdot5$ cm^{-1}, $931\cdot58$ and $968\cdot08$ cm^{-1}, 3414 cm^{-1} and $1627\cdot5$ cm^{-1}, and the a_1 vibrations are doubled by inversion. Assign symmetries to these frequencies and show that no more fundamentals are to be expected.

2 Classically, the probability of finding a particle at a point is inversely proportional to its velocity at that point. For a harmonic vibrator the energy is

$$E = \tfrac{1}{2}(kx^2 + mv^2).$$

Show that the probability is

$$p = \{(2E - kx^2)/m\}^{-1/2}$$

and the classical harmonic vibrator is constrained to lie within the parabola of figure 24.1, that is, $E \geqslant \tfrac{1}{2}kx^2$. Note that the quantised vibrator is not so constrained.

3   For CO the vibrational progression of the absorption spectrum is consistent with the vibrational energies (in eV):

$$E_n = 0 \cdot 26900(n + \tfrac{1}{2}) - 0 \cdot 00167(n + \tfrac{1}{2})^2.$$

Using equation (25.4), estimate the dissociation energy.

4   According to the *uncertainty principle*, the broadness of a peak ΔE is connected with the lifetime of the resulting state, t, by the relation $\Delta E = h/t$, where h is Planck's constant. The 0–4 vibrational component of the $(3\sigma^+)^{-1}$ band in the photoelectron spectrum of HBr is broadened by $0 \cdot 04$ eV; calculate the lifetime of the ion. The vibrational frequency of the ion is about 1400 cm^{-1} as judged from the vibrational separation in the spectrum. Calculate the number of vibrations that can occur within the lifetime of the ion.

5   By adding up the energies of the upper occupied orbitals derived from figure 33.3, plot the potential energy curve for allene. Notice how broad it is. Assume the frequency of the torsional mode to be 865 cm^{-1} and derive the energy of the first few vibrational levels. Plot them on the potential energy curve in the manner of figure 24.1, and estimate roughly the magnitude of the Jahn–Teller splitting of the first vibrational level.

6   Using table 22.1 show that vibrations of e symmetry are Jahn–Teller-active in the point group C_{3v}. How does this affect the spectrum of ammonia? Show that the symmetry of ammonia is lowered either to C_s ($E + \sigma_h$) or to C_1 (no symmetry) by e vibrations.

4 Spin–Orbit Coupling

36 The Spin–Orbit Coupling Constant

In the polyelectronic case the total spin quantum number, s, is written S, and m_s (the spin quantum number analogous to m in equation (6.6)) is written M_s. If the number of electrons is even, S is an integer; otherwise S is half-integral. M_s takes the values, S, $S-1$, $S-2$, ..., $-S$. Since angular momenta are vectors, they are denoted by the bold characters l, m, s, m_s, etc. The relationships between angular momenta and the corresponding magnetic moments are

$$\mu_s = -(e/m)s$$

$$\mu_l = -\tfrac{1}{2}(e/m)l$$

where e is the charge and m is the mass of the electron. The relationships between magnitudes and quantum numbers are

$$\mu_s = \frac{eh}{2\pi m}[s(s+1)]^{1/2}$$

$$\mu_l = \frac{eh}{4\pi m}[l(l+1)]^{1/2}.$$

The orbital motion of the electron carries it around the nucleus producing, at the electron, a magnetic flux $B = \mu_0 Z \mu_l/(2\pi r^3)$, where μ_0 is the permeability of free space, Z is the atomic number of the nucleus and r is the nuclear–electronic separation distance. In this B field, the potential energy of the spin magnetic moment is $-\mu_s \cdot B$. Hence the expression for the spin–orbit interaction energy is

$$E_{so} = \frac{-\mu_0 Z}{4\pi r^3}\mu_l \cdot \mu_s. \tag{36.1}$$

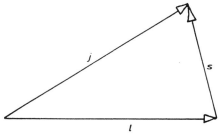

Figure 36.1. Vector addition of the orbital angular momentum, l, and the spin momentum, s, to give the resultant, j, for an electron. Only one figure is drawn, that of $l+s$, but in fact $j = l \pm s$.

Table 36.1. One-electron spin–orbit coupling constants (in eV) derived from atomic spectra (Moore 1952).

Configuration	Li	Be	B	C	N	O	F	Ne	Na
$K2p^1$	3×10^{-5}								
$K2s^12p^1$		2×10^{-4}	0·002						
$K2s^22p^1$			0·001	0·005					
$K2s^22p^2$				0·004	0·011				
$K2s^22p^3$					0·009	0·021			
$K2s^22p^4$						−0·019	−0·041		
$K2s^22p^5$							−0·033	−0·065	−0·113

	Na	Mg	Al	Si	P	S	Cl	Ar	K
$KL3p^1$	0·001	0·008							
$KL3s^13p^1$		0·005	0·015						
$KL3s^23p^1$			0·009	0·024					
$KL3s^23p^2$				0·018	0·039				
$KL3s^23p^3$					0·034	0·060			
$KL3s^23p^4$						−0·047	−0·082		
$KL3s^23p^5$							−0·073	−0·118	−0·178

	K	Ca	Ga	Ge	As	Se	Br	Kr	Rb
$KL3s^23p^64p^1$	0·005								
$KL4s^14p^1$		0·013							
$KLM4s^24p^1$			0·068						
$KLM4s^24p^2$				0·116	0·22				
$KLM4s^24p^3$					0·27				
$KLM4s^24p^4$						−0·21	−0·317		
$KLM4s^24p^5$							−0·305	−0·443	−0·609

	Sc	Ti	V	Cr	Mn	Fe	Co	Ni	Cu
$KL3d^14s^2$	0·008	0·023							
$KL3d^24s^2$		0·013							
$KL3d^34s^2$			0·020						
$KL3d^44s^2$				0·028					
$KL3d^54s^2$					0·030				
$KL3d^64s^2$						−0·048			
$KL3d^74s^2$							−0·064		
$KL3d^84s^2$								−0·074	
$KL3d^94s^2$									−0·102

	Rb	Sr	Cd	In	Sn	I	Xe	Cs
$KLM4s^24p^65p^1$	0·020							
$KLM4s^25s^15p^1$		0·048						
$KLMN5s^15p^1$			0·141					
$KLMN5s^25p^1$				0·182				
$KLMN5s^25p^2$					0·32			
$KLMN5s^25p^5$						−0·63	−0·87	−0·81

	Hg	Tl	Pb	Bi
$KLMN5s^25p^65d^96s^2$	−0·74			
$KLMNO6s^26p^1$		0·644		
$KLMNO6s^26p^2$			1·15	1·9
$KLMNO6s^26p^3$				1·17

There is a factor of $\frac{1}{2}$ in equation (36.1) that derives from a relativity effect. Coupling between the two momenta gives rise to a resultant vector, j (figure 36.1). Since this figure is a vector diagram, the cosine rule gives

$$j^2 = s^2 + l^2 - 2l \cdot s.$$

The spin–orbit coupling energy is proportional to $l \cdot s$ and therefore from the above,

$$E_{so} = \tfrac{1}{2}\xi(j^2 - l^2 - s^2)$$
$$= \tfrac{1}{2}\xi\{j(j+1) - s(s+1) - l(l+1)\}. \tag{36.2}$$

The *spin–orbit coupling constant*, ξ, is a constant for a given value of nuclear charge, Z, and the electron–nuclear distance, r. According to equation (36.2), if there are two states with the same values of l and s, but different values of j equal to j and $j-1$, then they are separated in energy by $j\xi$. This is the *Landé interval rule*.

For example, the value of ξ for caesium 6p can be calculated from the observed energies of the $j = \frac{1}{2}$ and the $j = \frac{3}{2}$ states of the $5p^6 6p$ configuration. These states give rise to a pair of lines in the optical spectrum at 1.386 eV $(j = \frac{1}{2})$ and 1.454 eV $(j = \frac{3}{2})$ (Moore 1952); hence $\xi = 0.068/1.5 = 0.045$ eV. Other values of ξ are given in table 36.1.

For partially filled shells, where 'holes' act as if they were positive electrons, the spin–orbit coupling constant is negative in sign. The observed spectroscopic lines are often due to mixtures of states with different quantum numbers, and consistent values of ξ are not then obtained from different pairs of lines. In a given configuration, say p^5 in the halogens, ξ is found to increase approximately as Z^2.

In the polyelectronic case the Landé interval rule can be written

$$E(J) - E(J-1) = \lambda J,$$

where λ replaces the single-electron constant, ξ. The relationship between the two constants is

$$\lambda M M_s = \sum_i \xi(m m_s)_i$$

and the summation includes all the electrons in the partially occupied shell: for example, for the ^3P state of a p^2 configuration (§ 10), the electrons can take the following values for the quantum numbers: $m = 1$, $m_s = \frac{1}{2}$ and $m = 0$, $m_s = \frac{1}{2}$. Hence

$$\lambda(1 \times 1) = \xi(1 \times \tfrac{1}{2}) + \xi(0 \times \tfrac{1}{2})$$
$$= \tfrac{1}{2}\xi.$$

For example, in the $5p^2$ configuration of tin there is a ^3P state with components separated by 0.21 eV $(J = 1$ and $J = 0)$ and by 0.22 eV $(J = 2$ and $J = 1)$. The derived values of λ are 0.21 and 0.105 eV, with an average of 0.16 eV. An average value of $\xi(5p)$ is therefore 0.32 eV.

It is often convenient to write the expression for the spin–orbit energy in the form

$$E_{so} = \xi \mathbf{l} \cdot \mathbf{s}$$

$$= \xi(m_x s_x + m_y s_y + m_z s_z)$$

$$= \xi\{\tfrac{1}{2}(m_x + im_y)(s_x - is_y) + \tfrac{1}{2}(m_x - im_y)(s_x + is_y) + m_z s_z\}$$

and hence the spin–orbit operator can be written

$$\xi\{\tfrac{1}{2}(\hat{M}_x + i\hat{M}_y)(\hat{S}_x - i\hat{S}_y) + \tfrac{1}{2}(\hat{M}_x - i\hat{M}_y)(\hat{S}_x + i\hat{S}_y) + \hat{M}_z\hat{S}_z\}$$

$$= \xi\{\tfrac{1}{2}\hat{M}_+\hat{S}_- + \tfrac{1}{2}\hat{M}_-\hat{S}_+ + \hat{M}_z\hat{S}_z\} \tag{36.3}$$

where $\hat{M}_+$ and $\hat{S}_+$ are the raising and $\hat{M}_-$ and $\hat{S}_-$ are the lowering operators (see Appendix V).

37 The Spin–Orbit Effect in Carbon and its Congeners

Having the valence configuration s^2p^2, the states and energies of C, Si, Ge, Sn and Pb are to be found in equations (11.8). According to these equations the interval ratio $(^1S - ^1D)/(^1D - ^3P) = 1\cdot5$, whereas the observed values are $1\cdot5$, $1\cdot48$, $1\cdot5$, $1\cdot38$ and $0\cdot62$ proceeding from C to Pb along the series. The decrease results from an increase in the spin–orbit interaction.

For ^3P the value of λ is $\xi/2$ and the spin–orbit coupling energies calculated by equation (36.2) are $-\xi$ ($^3P_0$), $-\tfrac{1}{2}\xi$ ($^3P_1$) and $\tfrac{1}{2}\xi$ ($^3P_2$). If the spin–orbit interaction is small enough that the theory of § 11 still holds, the energies of the states are therefore those of equation (11.8), plus the spin–orbit interaction energies. The energy of $^3P_0$ is therefore $E_0 + F_0 - 5F_2 - \xi$. It is noted that the 'centre of gravity' of the energies remains unaltered by the inclusion of the spin–orbit interaction if allowance is made for the $(2J + 1)$-fold degeneracy of the levels.

A large spin–orbit interaction causes the L and S quantum numbers to cease being constants of the motion of the electrons, and only J retains validity. A transition from L–S to J–J coupling ensues. In the J–J coupling scheme, the equivalent of table 10.1 for the p^2 configuration is table 37.1 (Condon and Shortley 1964). It is noteworthy that the number of states (each designated with a J value) is the same in J–J as in L–S coupling, so that either scheme is suitable for the labelling of states throughout the range from pure L–S to pure J–J coupling. It is

Table 37.1. One-electron functions for p^2; the J–J scheme.

M_J	$\frac{3}{2}, \frac{3}{2}$	$\frac{3}{2}, \frac{1}{2}$	$\frac{1}{2}, \frac{1}{2}$
		j, j'	
2	$(\frac{3}{2}, \frac{1}{2})$	$(\frac{3}{2}\ \frac{1}{2})$	
1	$(\frac{3}{2}, -\frac{1}{2})$	$(\frac{3}{2}, -\frac{1}{2}), (\frac{1}{2}, \frac{1}{2})$	
0	$(\frac{3}{2}, -\frac{3}{2}), (\frac{1}{2}, -\frac{1}{2})$	$(\frac{1}{2}, -\frac{1}{2}), (-\frac{1}{2}, \frac{1}{2})$	$(\frac{1}{2} -\frac{1}{2})$
-1	$(-\frac{3}{2}, \frac{1}{2})$	$(-\frac{3}{2}, \frac{1}{2}), (-\frac{1}{2}, -\frac{1}{2})$	
-2	$(-\frac{3}{2}, -\frac{1}{2})$	$(-\frac{3}{2}, -\frac{1}{2})$	
J	2, 0	2, 1	0

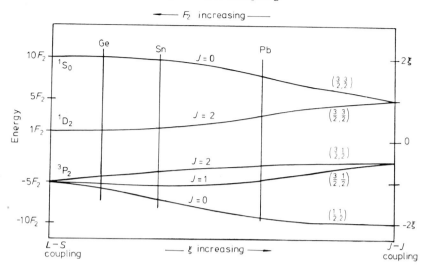

Figure 37.1. The transition from L–S to J–J coupling for the p^2 configuration.

clear that $^1S_0$ correlates with $J = 0$, $^1D_2$ with $J = 2$, and $^3P_{0,1,2}$ with $J = 0$, 1, 2. The energies in the J–J scheme are

$$E_{so} = \sum_{electrons} \tfrac{1}{2}\xi\{j(j+1) - l(l+1) - s(s+1)\}. \tag{37.1}$$

For example, the $J = 2, 0$ states arising from $j, j' = \tfrac{3}{2}, \tfrac{3}{2}$ have the energy

$$2 \times \tfrac{1}{2}\xi(\tfrac{3}{2} \times \tfrac{5}{2} - 1 \times 2 - \tfrac{1}{2} \times \tfrac{3}{2}) = \xi$$

and the other energies are $-\tfrac{1}{2}\xi$ and -2ξ for $J = 2$, 1 and $J = 0$, respectively.

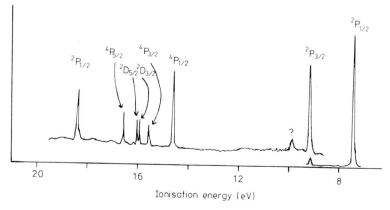

Figure 37.2. The photoelectron spectrum of Pb vapour at 715 °C using 21·21 eV radiation (Süzer *et al* 1975).

In the intermediate regions between L–S and J–J coupling, the energies are

$$E(J=0)=F_0+\tfrac{5}{2}F_2-\tfrac{1}{2}\xi\pm(\tfrac{225}{4}F_2^2+\tfrac{15}{2}F_2\xi+\tfrac{9}{4}\xi^2)^{1/2}$$

$$E(J=1)=F_0-5F_2-\tfrac{1}{2}\xi$$

$$E(J=2)=F_0-2F_2+\tfrac{1}{4}\xi\pm(9F_2^2-\tfrac{3}{2}F_2\xi+\tfrac{9}{16}\xi^2)^{1/2}.$$

The correlation between the two schemes is given in figure 37.1, where it can be seen that Pb is more than half-way towards pure J–J coupling. The photoelectron spectrum of Pb vapour at 715 °C is given in figure 37.2. The first pair of lines are for the ionisation

$$s^2p^2\rightarrow s^2p^1$$

giving ions in the states $^2P_{1/2}$ and $^2P_{3/2}$, which lie at 7·415 and 9·160 eV, respectively, in agreement with the Landé interval rule and a value $\xi=1·16$ eV. The relative intensity is 1:0·07, which has received the following explanation (Süzer *et al* 1975).

In pure L–S coupling the $^3P_0$ ground state of p^2 is composed equally of $j=\tfrac{1}{2}$ and $j'=\tfrac{3}{2}$ (equation (11.6)), each of which has the same chance of being ionised. Hence L–S coupling results in an equal intensity for the $^2P_{1/2}$ and the $^2P_{3/2}$ peaks. In J–J coupling, on the other hand, the ground state is $j=\tfrac{1}{2}$, $j'=\tfrac{1}{2}$ and only the $^2P_{1/2}$ line appears. In the range of intermediate coupling, the intensity of $^2P_{3/2}$ diminishes as ξ increases in magnitude. Calculations indicate the following relative intensities (Desclaux 1972): 0·496 (C), 0·479 (Si), 0·392 (Ge), 0·268 (Sn), 0·081 (Pb), and 0·008 (element 114) (element 114 is one of the superheavy elements conjectured to have some stability).

The foregoing theory is inadequate in one respect: no account has been made of the existence of configurations other than s^2p^2. The configuration p^4, for example, possesses ^1S, ^1D and ^3P states which mix with those of s^2p^2. If a mixture of configurations gives rise to the wavefunction Ψ with the mixing coefficient μ,

$$\Psi=\frac{\psi_a+\mu\psi_b}{(1+\mu^2)^{1/2}}$$

and the energy is

$$(E_a+2\mu H_{ab}+\mu^2 E_b)/(1+\mu^2).$$

Application of the variation theorem gives us

$$\mu=\frac{H_{ab}}{E-E_b}\simeq\frac{H_{ab}}{E_a-E_b}.$$

The above approximation is valid as long as μ is small; that is, as long as E_a-E_b is not close to zero. Those configurations close in energy to s^2p^2 and having states of the same designation will be the most important. The effects of this configuration interaction complicate the situation profoundly: for example, the interval ratios of 1·5 mentioned earlier in this section takes the value 1·13 in N^+ as a consequence.

The p^4 configuration is in fact too high in energy to mix very much into the ground state of carbon and its congeners, but the involvement of 6d in Pb is indicated by the presence of the lines labelled $^2D_{3/2}$ and $^2D_{5/2}$ in figure 37.2. In the optical spectrum of Pb^+ the lines for $6s^26d$ occur at 8·5478 eV ($^2D_{5/2}$) and 8·6440 eV ($^2D_{3/2}$). These energies are with respect to the $6s^26p$ ground state of Pb^+, but this itself is 7·415 eV above the $6s^26p$ ground state of Pb:

$$h\nu + Pb(6s^26p^2) \rightarrow Pb^+(6s^26p) + e^-.$$

The ionisation energy of the above process is 7·415 eV. Hence the ^2D states arising from

$$h\nu + Pb(6s^26p^2) \rightarrow Pb^+(6s^26d) + e^-$$

require, as observed, 15·963 eV and 16·059 eV. What is nominally $Pb(6s^26p^2)$ must therefore also contain some 6d character.

Ionisation of the 6s electrons produces terms of the designations $^{2,4}(S, P, D)$. Energies of these terms calculated by the above method are given in table 37·2. Since the ground state of Pb is $^3P_0$, the expected states of $Pb^+(6s6p^2)$ arising from it are obtained from the sum $^3P_0 + {}^2S_{1/2} = {}^{2,4}P_{1/2}$. These are both observed with high intensity.

Table 37.2. Ionisation energies (in eV) calculated for $Pb(6s^26p^2) \rightarrow Pb^+(6s6p^2)$. A tick indicates that the line has been observed in the photoelectron spectrum of the vapour (Süzer *et al* 1975).

$^4P_{1/2}$	14·593 ✓
$^4P_{3/2}$	15·611 ✓
$^4P_{5/2}$	16·575 ✓
$^2D_{3/2}$	17·713
$^2D_{5/2}$	18·443
$^2P_{1/2}$	18·353 ✓
$^2P_{3/2}$	20·388
$^2S_{1/2}$	20·342

The remaining terms in table 37.2 require configuration interaction. For example, the ^2D terms from the ionisation of $6s^2$ cannot derive from the $^3P_0$ state, but come from $^1D_2 + {}^2S_{1/2}$. Since the j values are both $\frac{3}{2}$ for the 6p electrons in the $^1D_2$ state, and they are both $\frac{1}{2}$ in the $^3P_0$ state, this particular interaction requires the excitation of two electrons and therefore has a low mixing coefficient. The corresponding lines are not seen in the photoelectron spectrum.

The $^4P_{3/2}$ and $^4P_{5/2}$ lines arise from $^3P_1 + {}^2S_{1/2}$ and $^3P_2 + {}^2S_{1/2}$, respectively. In the J–J scheme this involves the $\frac{1}{2}, \frac{3}{2}$ configuration for the $6p^2$ electrons, that is, the excitation of one electron from the $\frac{1}{2}, \frac{1}{2}$ configuration.

38 Double Groups

As mentioned in §§ 9 and 23, the total wavefunction consists of an electronic part, a nuclear part and a spin part, $\Psi = \psi \theta \Omega$. As far as symmetry properties are concerned, the spin part of the function, Ω, is totally symmetric if the spin–orbit interaction is small, that is, its symmetry is ignored; otherwise the symmetry of the spin function must be explicitly considered. However, there is found to be a complication.

For a polyelectronic atom the total quantum number, J, comprises L, which is always integral, and S, which is sometimes integral and sometimes half-integral. The total momentum is quantised,

$$\langle \Omega | \hat{M}_J | \Omega \rangle = M_J h / (2\pi)$$

where the $\hat{M}_J$ operator is analogous to $\hat{M}_z$. Its eigenfunctions are $\exp(iM_J\phi)$. There are $2J + 1$ values of M_J ranging from J to $-J$. Rotation of $\exp(iM_J\phi)$ by the angle θ gives the result $\exp[iM_J(\phi + \theta)]$, and for the rotation of the set of $2J + 1$ functions, the matrix is

$$\begin{pmatrix} \exp(iJ\theta) & 0 & 0 & \dots \\ 0 & \exp[i(J-1)\theta] & 0 & \dots \\ 0 & 0 & \exp[i(J-2)\theta]\dots \\ & & \text{etc} \end{pmatrix}$$

which has the character

$$\frac{\sin (J + \frac{1}{2})\theta}{\sin (\frac{1}{2}\theta)}.$$

The complication consists in the fact that if J is half-integral, the above character has the opposite signs for rotations by θ and by $\theta + 2\pi$. For the space function ψ and θ, such rotations have the same character.

Table 38.1. Character table for the C_{3v} double group.

C_{3v}	E	$2C_3(z)$	$3\sigma_v$	R	C_3R
A_1	1	1	1	1	1
A_2	1	1	-1	1	1
E	2	-1	0	2	-1
$E_{1/2}$	2	1	0	-2	-1
$E_{3/2}$	2	-2	0	-2	2

Recognition of the failure of a 2π rotation to regenerate the same half-integral spin causes it to be designated as a new operation, denoted R. Addition of this new operation to the spatial point groups gives the *extended* or *double point groups*. For example, in C_{3v} where the operations are E, C_3 and σ (table 22.1), the double group comprises these plus R, $C_3 \times R$ and $\sigma \times R$. The last of these, however, is not different from σ because the σ operation is not complicated by differences in the behaviour of half-integral and integral spins (neither is the rotation by the angle $\theta = \pi$). The characters for the C_{3v} double group are given in table 38.1; others can be found in Herzberg (1966).

39 The Boron Trihalides

Boron tri-iodide, BI_3, is a colourless solid which melts at 43 °C; BBr_3 is a liquid at ordinary temperatures, and the lower halides are both gases. They are all planar (point group D_{3h}) and sufficiently volatile for the measurement of their photoelectron spectra (figure 39.1).

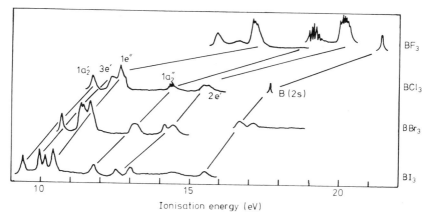

Figure 39.1. The photoelectron spectra of the boron trihalides (Potts *et al* 1970). Under conditions of high resolution, further structure appears in the spectrum of BI_3.

The total spin quantum number of the ions resulting from the photoelectric effect is $\frac{1}{2}$ since the neutral molecules have closed shells. The spin function therefore belongs to the $e_{1/2}$ representation of the D_{3h} double group (table 39.1). The characters of the total wavefunction—space × spin—are found from the characters of the direct products. For space functions of symmetry e'' we obtain

$$e'' \times e_{1/2} = e_{1/2} + e_{3/2}$$

and for e'

$$e' \times e_{1/2} = e_{3/2} + e_{5/2}.$$

Table 39.1. The D_{3h} double group.

D_{3h}	E	$S_3(z)$	$C_3(z)$	$\sigma(xy)$	C_2	σ_v	R	S_3R	C_3R
A'_1	1	1	1	1	1	1	1	1	1
A'_2	1	1	1	1	-1	-1	1	1	1
A''_1	1	-1	1	-1	1	-1	1	-1	1
A''_2	1	-1	1	-1	-1	1	1	-1	1
E''	2	1	-1	-2	0	0	2	1	-1
E'	2	-1	-1	2	0	0	2	-1	-1
$E_{1/2}$	2	$\sqrt{3}$	1	0	0	0	-2	$-\sqrt{3}$	-1
$E_{3/2}$	2	0	-2	0	0	0	-2	0	2
$E_{5/2}$	2	$-\sqrt{3}$	1	0	0	0	-2	$\sqrt{3}$	-1

Apparently, the result of the inclusion of the symmetry of the half-integral spin is, in effect, a change in symmetry, and the degeneracy of the e' and e" orbitals is raised. The e orbitals of the double group are in fact doubly degenerate in the absence of a magnetic field, but this will not concern us. The restrictions of the mixing of, for example, a'_1 and a'_2 are relaxed on passing to the double group, since both finish up as $e_{1/2}$. Any $e_{3/2}$ orbital in the double group can have parentage from both e" and e' orbitals of the single group. There are thus two effects that can be anticipated as the spin–orbit interaction increases from BF_3 to BI_3: the mixing of orbitals and the splitting of bands.

The magnitude of the spin–orbit interaction depends upon the halogen, since the coupling constant is very small for the boron atom. For the 2e' bands the observed splittings are 0.5 eV (BI_3), 0.31 eV (BBr_3) and 0.18 eV (BCl_3), compared with the values $\xi = 0.63$, 0.31 and 0.08 eV. It is probable that the splitting in BCl_3 is not caused by spin–orbit interaction at all, but by the Jahn–Teller effect which quenches the spin–orbit interaction (see § 40).

The halogenic p orbitals in the boron trihalides can be divided into three groups (figure 39.2);

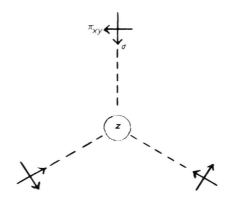

Figure 39.2. Disposition of the halogenic p orbitals in the boron trihalides.

(π_z) These are directed along the z axis, they have pi orientation with respect to the central atom, and span a''_2 and e".
(σ) These are in the molecular plane, they have sigma orientation with respect to the central atom, and span a'_1 and e'.
(π_{xy}) These are in the molecular plane, they have pi orientation with respect to the central atom, and span a'_2 and e'.

The e" orbitals are comprised of only a single p orbital per halogen atom (p_z), the simplest of which is

$$\frac{1}{\sqrt{2}}\{p(z)_1 - p(z)_2\}$$

where $p(z)_1$ is on halogen atom 1, etc. In § 5 it was demonstrated that at least two atomic orbitals are necessary for there to be an angular momentum about the nucleus. Without such a momentum there can be no spin–orbit interaction, and hence there can be no first-order splitting of the e'' orbital in the case of the boron trihalides.

In the second-order case we might expect some splitting of e'' by the mixing of its $e_{3/2}$ component with those of e' orbitals, but the effect is likely to be small.

Orbitals of e' symmetry are subject to a first-order spin–orbit interaction. Three peaks are found in the region of the BI_3 spectrum corresponding to the ionisation of the $1e''$ and $3e'$ orbitals: their assignment has been the subject of differing opinions (Potts *et al* 1970, Manne *et al* 1975). The spectra of Potts *et al* (1970) are shown in figure 39.1.

40   The Ham Effect

If a Jahn–Teller effect removes the degeneracy upon which spin–orbit interaction depends, it is clear that there cannot be both strong Jahn–Teller and spin–orbit effects present at one and the same time. A strong spin–orbit interaction similarly quenches the Jahn–Teller effect, and any pair of operators having only off-diagonal components quench each other in this fashion. This is known as the *Ham effect*.

For example, the dynamic Jahn–Teller effect in the boron trihalides is engendered by e' vibrations (§ 35) which lower the symmetry to C_{2v} in which all irreducible representations are non-degenerate. Vibrations of e' symmetry, however, are rendered inactive by spin–orbit interaction which produces $e_{1/2}$, $e_{3/2}$ and $e_{5/2}$ in the D_{3h} double group from orbitals of e' and e'' symmetry. According to the argument given in § 34, the symmetries of possible vibrations producing the Jahn–Teller effect can be derived from the direct products, namely,

$$e_{1/2} \times e_{1/2} = a_2' + e''$$

$$e_{3/2} \times e_{3/2} = a_2' + a_1'' + a_2''$$

$$e_{5/2} \times e_{5/2} = a_2' + e''.$$

No e' vibration is seen among the above.

Competition of another kind is found in the alkyl halides, RX. Spin–orbit interaction of the halogenic p orbitals is in competition with conjugation with the orbitals of the alkyl group, R. Suppose that there is an alkyl orbital, ϕ, degenerate with p_x and p_y, where the p orbitals are perpendicular to the R—X bond. In general, since one of the p orbitals is antisymmetric and one is symmetric with respect to reflection in a plane through the bond, it is possible for one to interact with ϕ whilst the other does not, depending on the parity of ϕ with respect to this particular plane. Let us take the case in which p_x interacts with ϕ, where the resonance integral is β. In addition, p_x and p_y are connected through the spin–orbit interaction, $\xi l \cdot s$, which shall be written Z for brevity. The determinant (§ 34) becomes

$$\begin{array}{ccc} p_x & p_y & \phi \end{array}$$
$$\begin{vmatrix} (H_0 - E) & Z & \beta \\ Z & (H_0 - E) & 0 \\ \beta & 0 & (H_0 - E) \end{vmatrix} = 0.$$

The solutions give the non-bonding orbital,

$$(\beta/C)p_y - (Z/C)\phi \qquad\qquad (40.1)$$

where $C^2 = \beta^2 + Z^2$. The energy of this orbital is H_0. In addition, we have

$$(1/\sqrt{2})\left\{ \pm p_x + \frac{Z}{C}p_y + \frac{\beta}{C}\phi \right\} \qquad\qquad (40.2)$$

where the energy is $H_0 \mp C$.

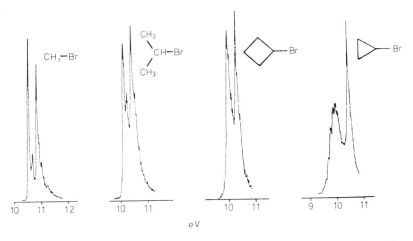

Figure 40.1. The first pair of bands in the photoelectron spectra of some alkyl bromides (Brogli and Heilbronner 1971).

The first band in the spectrum (figure 40.1) is due to the antibonding orbital of energy $H_0 + C$, and the second is due to the non-bonding orbital. The energy gap between them is almost a constant regardless of the nature of R (0·3 eV for Br, 0·6 eV for I), and therefore $\beta^2 + Z^2$ is constant, that is, a reduction in Z accompanies an increase in β. This can be attributed to the Ham effect.

It has been pointed out (Brogli and Heilbronner 1971) that the presence of vibrational structure on the first pair of bands in the RX spectra indicates that the alkyl group is indeed conjugated to p_x and to p_y. This vibrational structure is most marked on the band of lowest ionisation energy where it causes broadening: for example, in cyclopropyl bromide. That the second band remains sharp is attributed to its non-bonding nature.

One criterion of whether an orbital is bonding or not is whether or not it has an appreciable *bond order*, defined as the product of the coefficients in the molecular orbital wavefunction of the constituent atomic orbitals. Thus the bond order between atoms numbered 1 and 2 is $c_1 c_2$ for each electron in the orbital of wavefunction

$$\ldots c_1 \phi_i + c_2 \phi_2 \ldots$$

For the non-bonding orbital, the bond order as given by equation (40.1) is $\beta Z/C^2$, which is small in magnitude because both β and Z are small. On the other hand, equation (40.2) gives $-\beta/(\sqrt{2}C)$ for the bond order, which is a relatively large term.

41 The Halides of Methane

The first pair of bands in CH_3I discussed in § 40 arises from the ionisation of an orbital of e symmetry (point group C_{3v}; table 38.1). Such an orbital is susceptible to both the dynamic Jahn–Teller effect and spin–orbit interactions. As we have seen, the Jahn–Teller effect is in fact quenched by the spin–orbit interaction; the splitting of 0·6 eV (figure 4.3) is largely due to the latter, although some conjugation between the methyl group and the halogen has to be taken into account.

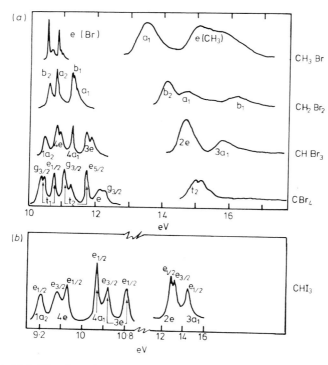

Figure 41.1. The photoelectron spectra of halides of methane. The spectra in (*a*) are from Potts *et al* (1970) and those in (*b*) are from Manne *et al* (1975).

At the higher ionisation energies another orbital of e symmetry is found (figure 41.1) which contains little halogenic character and possesses a band in the spectrum with two broad humps separated by about 0·9 eV in both CH_3I and CH_3Br. The splitting is evidently caused by the Jahn–Teller effect rather than spin–orbit interaction.

Table 41.1. The T_d double group.

T_d	E	C_3	σ_d	S_4	C_2	R	C_3^2R	S_4^3R	
A_1	1	1	1	1	1	1	1	1	$x^2+y^2+z^2$
A_2	1	1	-1	-1	1	1	1	-1	
E	2	-1	0	0	2	2	-1	0	$x^2-y^2, 2z^2-x^2-y^2$
T_1	3	0	-1	1	-1	3	0	1	R_x, R_y, R_z
T_2	3	0	1	-1	-1	3	0	-1	x, y, z, xy, xz, yz
$E_{1/2}$	2	1	0	$\sqrt{2}$	0	-2	-1	$-\sqrt{2}$	
$E_{5/2}$	2	1	0	$-\sqrt{2}$	0	-2	-1	$\sqrt{2}$	
$G_{3/2}$	4	-1	0	0	0	-4	1	0	

In T_d symmetry (table 41.1) all degenerate orbitals can undergo Jahn–Teller splitting but only those of threefold degeneracy are susceptible to the spin effect:

$$e_{1/2} \times e = g_{3/2}$$

$$e_{1/2} \times t_1 = e_{1/2} + g_{3/2}$$

$$e_{1/2} \times t_2 = e_{5/2} + g_{3/2}.$$

In the spectrum of CBr_4 there is a separation of $0·37$ eV between the $g_{3/2}$ and $e_{1/2}$ components of the first peak of t_1 symmetry in the spectrum (figure 41.1). All the $g_{3/2}$ peaks undergo a further small splitting, possibly due to the dynamic Jahn–Teller effect. The symmetrised direct product (see Appendix IV) for the $g_{3/2}$ representation is

$$g_{3/2} \times g_{3/2} = a_2 + 2t_1 + t_2$$

and t_2 vibrations lower the symmetry to C_{3v}, in which the $g_{3/2}$ orbitals become $e_{1/2}$ and $e_{3/2}$. In CCl_4 (figure 41.2) there is little evidence of spin–orbit interaction in the spectrum, but only a moderate Jahn–Teller interaction in the $3t_2$ and $1e$ bands.

The spectra of CHI_3 and $CHBr_3$ bear many points of comparison with BI_3 and BBr_3. In the chloroform analogues there is an extra pair of electrons present

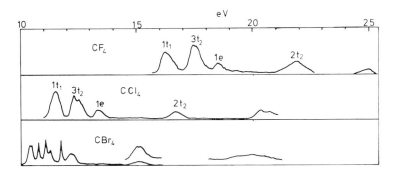

Figure 41.2. The photoelectron spectra of the tetrahalides of carbon (Potts *et al* 1970).

occupying the $4a_1$ orbital which shows up as an extra peak in the spectrum (compare figures 39.1 and 41.1). The correlation between the two sets of orbitals is $1a_2' \rightarrow 1a_2$; $3e' \rightarrow 4e$; $1e'' \rightarrow 3e$, etc. A difference between the two sets of spectra is the lack of splitting in the e'' orbitals of BX_3 discussed in § 39. In CHI_3, spin–orbit interaction has advanced to such an extent that only the classification of the double group is meaningful, and conjectures as to which peaks are derived from particular peaks of the $CHBr_3$ and $CHCl_3$ spectra are probably unproductive. For example, it has been calculated (Manne *et al* 1975) that the '$4a_1$' orbital ($e_{1/2}$ in the double group) has only 70% of $4a_1$ character (in the C_{3v} double group appropriate to CHI_3^+, $e_{1/2}$ arises from a_1, a_2 and e orbitals of the single group).

42   Inner Shells

When electrons lie inside the valence shell their interaction with electrons in adjacent atoms is not necessarily insignificant, although it is small compared with that of the valence electrons themselves. The d^{10} subshell of Zn, Cd and Hg is a case in point. Here the inner shell can be anticipated to lie about 10 eV below the valence shell (see Appendix III).

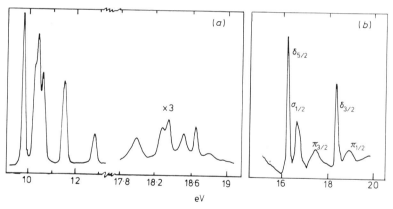

Figure 42.1. (*a*) The spectrum of ZnI_2 (Orchard and Richardson 1975) showing five peaks in the $3d^{10}$ ionisation regions around 18 eV. The intensities of the 3d peaks have been drawn three times larger relative to the valence shell peaks. (*b*) Photoelectron spectrum of CH_3HgCN (Burroughs *et al* 1974) showing the $Hg(5d^{10})$ ionisation peaks and possible assignments.

In the linear halides such as ZnI_2, the peaks for the ionisation of the 3d subshell are to be found at about 18 eV (figure 42.1). The irreducible representations spanned in $D_{\infty h}$ by d orbitals are δ_g, π_g and σ_g^+ (p 111), giving in the double group for the ion

$$e_{1/2} \times \pi_g = e_{1/2} + e_{3/2}$$

$$e_{1/2} \times \sigma_g^+ = e_{1/2}$$

$$e_{1/2} \times \delta_g = e_{3/2} + e_{5/2}.$$

Table 42.1. Direct products for D_∞.

	Σ^+	Σ^-	Π	Δ	$\cdots$	$E_{1/2}$	$E_{3/2}$	$E_{5/2}$
Σ^+	Σ^+	Σ^-	Π	Δ	$\cdots$	$E_{1/2}$	$E_{3/2}$	$E_{5/2}$
Σ^-		Σ^+	Π	Δ	$\cdots$	$E_{1/2}$	$E_{3/2}$	$E_{5/2}$
Π			$\Sigma^+, \Sigma^-, \Delta$	Π, ϕ		$E_{1/2}, E_{3/2}$	$E_{1/2}, E_{5/2}$	$E_{3/2}, E_{7/2}$
Δ				$\Sigma^+, \Sigma^-, \Gamma$		$E_{3/2}, E_{5/2}$	$E_{3/2}, E_{7/2}$	$E_{1/2}, E_{9/2}$
$\vdots$						$\vdots$	$\vdots$	$\vdots$
$E_{1/2}$						Σ^+, Σ^-, Π	Π, Δ	Δ, ϕ
$E_{3/2}$							Σ^+, Σ^-, ϕ	Π, Γ
$E_{5/2}$								Σ^+, Σ^-, H

Five peaks are observed in the spectrum (figure 42.1), which implies that both the molecular symmetry and the spin–orbit interaction have taken effect. In the absence of a molecular field the spectrum would contain only the twin peaks of $^2D_{3/2}$ and $^2D_{5/2}$.

The ligand orbitals span π and σ leaving the δ_g component of the central atom non-bonding, so that δ_g is expected to have a sharp peak in the spectrum. There are two such peaks in figure 42.1 for CH_3HgCN, which are separated by just over 2 eV. The implied spin–orbit coupling constant is $\xi = -0.8$ eV. Tentative assignments of the bands (Burroughs *et al* 1974) are given in figure 42.1.

43 The Spin–Orbit Effect in O_2 and its Congeners

The configuration of O_2, S_2, Se_2 and Te_2 is π_g^2, plus a core of filled shells. The first band in the spectrum is therefore expected to be associated with the ionic states $^2\Pi_{g,\frac{1}{2}}$ and $^2\Pi_{g,\frac{3}{2}}$. In the absence of spin–orbit interaction only one peak results, but on going along the series a separation ensues as the spin–orbit coupling constant increases in magnitude (figure 43.1). The situation is similar to that discussed for Pb

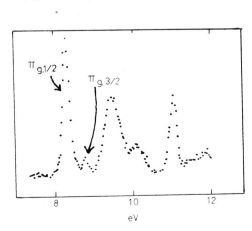

Figure 43.1. The photoelectron spectrum of Te_2 showing the separation of the $\Pi_{g,\frac{1}{2}}$ and the $\Pi_{g,\frac{3}{2}}$ peaks (Berkowitz 1975). The specimen was prepared by the volatilisation of tellurium at 400 °C.

and its congeners in § 37, where L–S coupling predicts equal intensities for the two components but the spin–orbit interaction causes the $^2\Pi_{g,\frac{3}{2}}$ peak to lose intensity. The observed ratios of the intensities of the components are given in table 43.1.

Table 43.1. Calculated values of $(a/b)^2$ and the observed ratios, $\Pi_{g,\frac{1}{2}}/\Pi_{g,\frac{3}{2}}$, of the intensities of the components of the first band in the spectrum of O_2, etc.

	ξ (eV)	$(a/b)^2$	Observed ratio
O_2	0·02	1·05	1·00[a]
S_2	0·05	1·1	1·2[a]
Se_2	0·21	1·7	2·0[a]
Te_2	0·4	2·6	10[a]
TeO	—	—	15[b]
Po_2	1·7	19·1	—

[a] Lee *et al* (1976).
[b] Potts and Williams (1976).

The molecular ground state is $^3\Sigma_g^-$, which arises from the combination of a pair of π_g space functions and two spins. The direct product of the space functions in the $D_{\infty h}$ space group is

$$\Pi_g \times \Pi_g = \Sigma_g^+ + \Delta_g + \Sigma_g^-$$

where the first pair is symmetric and Σ_g^- is antisymmetric (see Appendix IV). The spin functions α and β have the following possible combinations (the first three are symmetric and the last is antisymmetric with regard to the exchange of an electron from one function to another):

$$\left.\begin{array}{c} \alpha\beta + \beta\alpha \\ \alpha\alpha \\ \beta\beta \end{array}\right\} \text{triplet}$$

$$\alpha\beta - \beta\alpha \quad \text{singlet}$$

Since, by the Pauli principle, the overall function must be antisymmetric, the correct combinations of space and spin functions give $^1\Sigma_g^+$, $^1\Delta_g$ and $^3\Sigma_g^-$.

In pure L–S coupling we can take the orbital momentum of the π_g orbital to be directed along the molecular axis in either the positive or the negative direction, giving us either π^+ or π^-. We shall take the spin function α to imply the same orientation as π^+ and β to imply the same as π^-. Thus the j value of the combination $\pi^+\alpha$ is $\frac{3}{2}$, and the j value of $\pi^-\alpha$ is $-\frac{1}{2}$. It is convenient to write $\bar{\pi}^+$ for the combination $\pi^+\beta$, and $\bar{\pi}^-$ for $\pi^-\beta$, leaving $\pi^+\alpha$ to be written simply as π^+ and $\pi^-\alpha$ as π^-.

The Σ_g states are derived from the $\pi^+\pi^-$ combination of space functions whereas the $^1\Delta_g$ derives from $\pi^+\pi^+$ and $\pi^-\pi^-$. This should be clear from a consideration of table 43.2, which is analogous to table 10.1. Hence, for the ground state of the

Table 43.2. One-electron functions for π^2 in the diatomic case.

M_J	M_S		
	1	0	-1
2		$(\pi^+, \bar{\pi}^+)$	
0	(π^+, π^-)	$(\pi^+, \bar{\pi}^-), (\bar{\pi}^+, \pi^-)$	$(\bar{\pi}^+, \bar{\pi}^-)$
-2		$(\pi^-, \bar{\pi}^-)$	

molecule we derive the function

$$\psi(^3\Sigma_g^-) = \tfrac{1}{2}(\pi^+\pi^- - \pi^-\pi^+)(\alpha\beta + \beta\alpha)$$

$$= \tfrac{1}{2}(\pi^+\bar{\pi}^- + \bar{\pi}^+\pi^- - \pi^-\bar{\pi}^+ - \bar{\pi}^-\pi^+) \tag{43.1}$$

$$= \tfrac{1}{2}\{(\tfrac{3}{2}, -\tfrac{3}{2}) + (\tfrac{1}{2}, -\tfrac{1}{2}) - (-\tfrac{1}{2}, \tfrac{1}{2}) - (-\tfrac{3}{2}, \tfrac{3}{2})\}. \tag{43.2}$$

It is apparent that in terms of j–j coupling, the ground state is composed equally of $(\tfrac{3}{2}, \tfrac{3}{2})$ and $(\tfrac{1}{2}, \tfrac{1}{2})$ combinations as long as it is purely of $^3\Sigma_g^-$ character. In the absence of spin–orbit interaction, ionisation of one π_g electron therefore produces equal intensities of $^2\Pi_{g,\frac{1}{2}}$ and $^2\Pi_{g,\frac{3}{2}}$. For simplicity, we can in fact write

$$\psi(^3\Sigma_g^-) = (1/\sqrt{2})\{\phi(\tfrac{1}{2}, \tfrac{1}{2}) + \phi(\tfrac{3}{2}, \tfrac{3}{2})\} \tag{43.3}$$

where

$$\phi(\tfrac{1}{2}, \tfrac{1}{2}) = (1/\sqrt{2})\{(\tfrac{1}{2}, -\tfrac{1}{2}) - (-\tfrac{1}{2}, \tfrac{1}{2})\}$$

$$\phi(\tfrac{3}{2}, \tfrac{3}{2}) = (1/\sqrt{2})\{(\tfrac{3}{2}, -\tfrac{3}{2}) - (-\tfrac{3}{2}, \tfrac{3}{2})\}.$$

The wavefunction for $\psi(^1\Sigma_g^+)$ is found in exactly the same manner to be

$$\psi(^1\Sigma_g^+) = \tfrac{1}{2}(\pi^+\pi^- + \pi^-\pi^+)(\alpha\beta - \beta\alpha)$$

$$= \tfrac{1}{2}(\pi^+\bar{\pi}^- - \bar{\pi}^+\pi^- + \pi^-\bar{\pi}^+ - \bar{\pi}^-\pi^+) \tag{43.4}$$

$$= (1/\sqrt{2})\{\phi(\tfrac{3}{2}, \tfrac{3}{2}) - \phi(\tfrac{1}{2}, \tfrac{1}{2})\} \tag{43.5}$$

and it is clear that this function also consists equally of $j = \tfrac{1}{2}$ and $j = \tfrac{3}{2}$ components.

However the spin–orbit interaction results in the admixture of some $\psi(^1\Sigma_g^+)$ into the $^3\Sigma_g^-$ around state;

$$\psi\,(\text{ground}) = c_1\psi(^3\Sigma_g^-) + c_2\psi(^1\Sigma_g^+). \tag{43.6}$$

Alternatively, we can write

$$\psi\,(\text{ground}) = a\phi(\tfrac{1}{2}, \tfrac{1}{2}) + b\phi(\tfrac{3}{2}, \tfrac{3}{2}). \tag{43.7}$$

The expansion of equation (43.6) using (43.3) and (43.5) gives

$$\psi\,(\text{ground}) = \frac{c_1}{\sqrt{2}}\{\phi(\tfrac{1}{2}, \tfrac{1}{2}) + \phi(\tfrac{3}{2}, \tfrac{3}{2})\} + \frac{c_2}{\sqrt{2}}\{\phi(\tfrac{3}{2}, \tfrac{3}{2}) - \phi(\tfrac{1}{2}, \tfrac{1}{2})\} \tag{43.8}$$

and equating the coefficients of the functions in equations (43.7) and (43.8) gives

$$a = \frac{1}{\sqrt{2}}(c_1 - c_2)$$

$$b = \frac{1}{\sqrt{2}}(c_1 + c_2).$$

The relative intensity of the $\Pi_{g,\frac{1}{2}}$ and the $\Pi_{g,\frac{3}{2}}$ peaks in the spectrum of O_2, etc, is given by the ratio

$$(a/b)^2 = \left\{\frac{c_1 - c_2}{c_1 + c_2}\right\}^2 \tag{43.9}$$

as can be seen in equation (43.7).

In order to find the values of c_1 and c_2 it is necessary to inquire into the matrix elements connected with $\psi(^3\Sigma_g^-)$ and $\psi(^1\Sigma_g^+)$; these are of course the spin–orbit coupling term given by $\xi \mathbf{l} \cdot \mathbf{s}$ and the electron–electron repulsion term given by $\hat{q}$ (§ 11).

It is readily shown (see § 11) that the electron–electron repulsion energies are

$$\langle \psi(^3\Sigma_g^-)|\hat{q}|\psi(^3\Sigma_g^-)\rangle = J - K$$

$$\langle \psi(^1\Sigma_g^+)|\hat{q}|\psi(^1\Sigma_g^+)\rangle = J + K$$

and the off-diagonal $\langle \psi(^1\Sigma_g^+)|\hat{q}|\psi(^3\Sigma_g^-)\rangle$ is zero.

On the other hand, only the off-diagonal elements are nonzero for the spin–orbit interaction (see Appendix VI), and they have the value ξ. The determinant resulting from these considerations is

$$
\begin{array}{cc}
^3\Sigma_g^- & ^1\Sigma_g^+ \\
\end{array}
$$
$$
\begin{vmatrix}
-K-E & \xi \\
\xi & K-E
\end{vmatrix} = 0
$$

and the energies are

$$E = \pm(K^2 + \xi^2)^{1/2}.$$

From equation (43.6) and the above result,

$$c_1/c_2 = \frac{-K - (K^2 + \xi^2)^{1/2}}{\xi}$$

for the ground state. From equation (43.9) we can now calculate the relative intensity of the $\Pi_{g,\frac{1}{2}}$ and the $\Pi_{g,\frac{3}{2}}$ components of the spectrum.

The foregoing theory will lose accuracy as the spin–orbit coupling increases, and it is therefore not surprising that the best results are found for S_2 and Se_2 (table 43.1). The results in table 43.1 were obtained using the value $K = 0.82$ eV obtained from the optical spectrum of O_2 ($^1\Sigma_g^+$ being found at 1·64 eV). Unfortunately, the other members of the series have complex spectra in which the term energies could not be found, and it was necessary to use the same value of K throughout which introduces another error.

Problems

1 From the following energies (in eV) of the lines observed in the optical spectra of the elements calculate the one-electron spin–orbit coupling constant, ξ. Calculate ξ/Z^2 in each case and see whether this is a constant.

	Z	$^3P_0$	$^3P_1$	$^3P_2$
C	6	0·00	0·0020	0·0054
Si	14	0·00	0·0096	0·0277
Ge	32	0·00	0·0691	0·1748
Sn	50	0·00	0·2097	0·4249
Pb	82	0·00	0·9692	1·3201

2 Using the following table of energies (in eV) derived from the analysis of the optical spectra of Sn and Sn^+, calculate the first few lines in the photoelectron spectrum of Sn. Comment on the anticipated relative intensities of the lines.

The ionisation energy $Sn(5s^2 5p^2) \rightarrow Sn^+(5s^2 5p^1)^2P_{1/2}$ is 7·342 eV. The observed energies for Sn^+ are

$$5s^2 5p^1 (^2P_{3/2}) \qquad 0·5296$$

$$5s^1 5p^2 (^4P_{1/2}) \qquad 5·759$$

$$5s^1 5p^2 (^4P_{3/2}) \qquad 5·995$$

$$5s^1 5p^2 (^4P_{5/2}) \qquad 6·2878$$

3 In general, a ^3P state can be written $\phi(S, M_S) = \phi(1, 1)$. In table 10.1 we see that for the p^2 configuration, $\phi(1, 1) = (1^+, 0^+)$. Show that $\hat{S}_-(1^+, 0^+) = (1^-, 0^+) + (1^+, 0^-)$, and that

$$\hat{S}_- \phi(1, 1) = \sqrt{2} \phi(1, 0)$$

and hence that

$$\phi(1, 0) = (1/\sqrt{2})\{(1^-, 0^+) + (1^+, 0^-)\}.$$

4 Using table 39.1 derive the characters of the direct product of $e_{1/2}$ with the other irreducible representations and verify the following results:

$$e_{1/2} \times a_1' = e_{1/2}$$

$$e_{1/2} \times a_2' = e_{1/2}$$

$$e_{1/2} \times a_1'' = e_{5/2}$$

$$e_{1/2} \times a_2'' = e_{5/2}$$

$$e_{1/2} \times e' = e_{3/2} + e_{5/2}$$

$$e_{1/2} \times e'' = e_{1/2} + e_{3/2}.$$

5 The Angular Distribution of Photoelectrons

44 The Asymmetry Parameter, β

In this chapter we consider the direction taken by the photoelectron as it leaves the atom or molecule. Since we are interested in the gas phase, where molecules are freely rotating, the direction is measured with respect to either the direction of propagation or the plane of polarisation of the light beam. In figure 44.1 the direction of the photoelectron is along k, and the plane of polarisation of the light (the plane of the electric vector) is along j. The direction of the photoelectron is given by the angle θ between k and j.

Whether or not photoemission takes place in a preferred direction depends, among other things, on the time taken to complete the process. If autoionisation is taking place via an intermediate state with a lifetime greater than 10^{-13} s or so, there will be time enough for the molecule to rotate and the electrons will come out isotropically

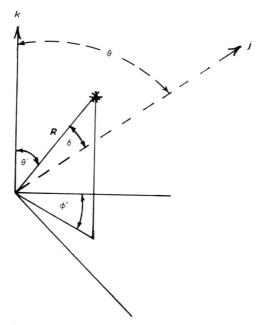

Figure 44.1. Angular dependence of photoemission. The propagation direction of the electron is along k and the direction of the electric vector of the light beam is along j.

from a specimen of gas. The direct photoelectric effect, however, which takes only 10^{-15} s to complete, is much too fast for the completion of a rotation.

As mentioned in § 7, the probability of emission depends upon the dipole moment operator, er, which can be related to figure 44.1. If j lies in the plane $\phi = 0$, and the molecule lies at the point R, θ', ϕ',

$$er = eR \cos \delta$$

$$= eR(\cos \theta \cos \theta' + \sin \theta \sin \theta' \cos \phi').$$

For the given small volume of space in which the molecule is situated the square of the above expression is proportional to the transition probability (equation (7.2)), giving us terms in $\cos^2 \theta$, $\sin^2 \theta$ and $\cos \theta \sin \theta$. That the last term is zero follows from the symmetry of the problem, since the emission probability must be independent of whether the polarisation vector is directed in the positive or negative sense along j for it is independent of the sign of θ. Hence the probability of emission must be an even function of θ, which is true for $\cos^2 \theta$ and $\sin^2 \theta$, but untrue for $\cos \theta \sin \theta$. The angular dependence now takes the form

$$p = A \cos^2 \theta + B \sin^2 \theta \tag{44.1}$$

where A and B are constants. The usual form of writing this relationship is

$$d\sigma/d\Omega = \frac{\sigma(\text{total})}{4\pi}(1 + \beta P_2) \tag{44.2}$$

where $d\sigma$ is the cross section for emission into the solid angle $d\Omega$. The *asymmetry*

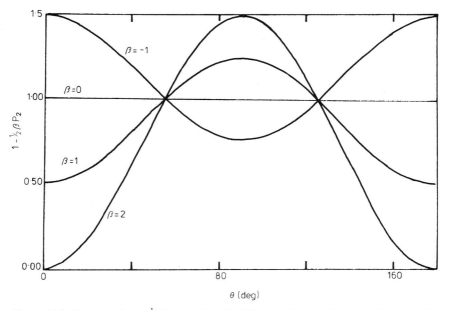

Figure 44.2. The quantity $1 - \frac{1}{2}\beta P_2$ (equation (44.3)), plotted against the angle θ between the propagation direction of the light beam and the direction of the photoelectron. At two angles the photocurrent is independent of β.

parameter, β, is a constant for a given molecule at fixed light energy and ionisation energy. The second-order Legendre polynomial, P_2, is given by

$$P_2 = \tfrac{1}{2}(3 \cos^2 \theta - 1).$$

If the light is unpolarised and θ is measured with respect to the direction of propagation of the beam,

$$d\sigma/d\Omega = \frac{\sigma(\text{total})}{4\pi}(1 - \tfrac{1}{2}\beta P_2). \qquad (44.3)$$

Since $d\sigma/d\Omega$ cannot be less than zero, it can be ascertained from equation (44.2) that β cannot lie outside the range of magnitudes -1 to 2. $d\sigma/d\Omega$ is sometimes called the *differential cross section*. This is plotted against θ for a number of different values of β in figure 44.2, where it is seen that there are 'magic angles', $54° 44'$ and $180 - 54° 44'$, at which the differential cross section is independent of θ. Unless a spectrometer operates ,at the magic angle, the relative intensity of peaks with different values of β will be incorrectly registered, but few instruments are designed with this in mind.

45 Angular Distribution in the Noble Gases

For an electron in an atomic p orbital the optical transition to either an s or a d orbital is allowed, that is, the transition dipole moment, $\boldsymbol{R}$, is finite:

$$\boldsymbol{R} = \langle \phi(\text{initial})|er|\phi(\text{final})\rangle.$$

Hence the ionisation of a p orbital is pictured as passing through two *channels*, $p \to ns$ and $p \to nd$, where the principal quantum number n in the second state differs from that in the first state. In general, the second orbital in a channel takes the value $l \pm 1$ for the azimuthal quantum number if l is the initial value (or $l \pm 3, l \pm 5$ with diminishing magnitude of R).

Each channel can be regarded as a wave having a characteristic asymmetry parameter. For the $l+1$ wave,

$$\beta = \frac{l+2}{2l+1}$$

and for the $l-1$ wave,

$$\beta = \frac{l(l-1)}{2l+1}.$$

Thus we have

$$s \to p, \qquad \beta = 2$$
$$p \to s, \qquad \beta = 0$$
$$p \to d, \qquad \beta = 1$$
$$d \to p, \qquad \beta = 0\cdot4$$
$$d \to f, \qquad \beta = 0\cdot8.$$

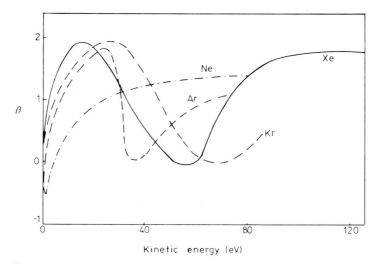

Figure 45.1. Variation with kinetic energy of the asymmetry parameter, β, for the outer p electrons of the noble gases (obtained with the use of synchrotron radiation) (Marr 1976).

Interference between channels (if more than one is possible) complicates the matter, and

$$\beta = \frac{l(l-1)R_{l-1}^2 + (l+1)(l+2)R_{l+1}^2 - 6l(l+1)R_{l-1}R_{l+1}\cos\Delta}{(2l+1)[lR_{l-1}^2 + (l+1)R_{l+1}^2]} \tag{45.1}$$

where Δ is the difference in phase angle between the two channels. This angle varies with the energy of the photoelectron (and therefore with the energy of the ionising radiation), and hence β is found to depend upon the radiation energy (figure 45.1).

With the exception of helium, the band of lowest energy in the spectrum of the noble gases is due to the ionisation of a full p shell which gives $^2P_{1/2}$ and $^2P_{3/2}$ components. Equation (45.1) is found to be inadequate in a number of respects: for example, it is based upon L–S coupling and is invalid in the presence of a large spin–orbit interaction. Also, the one-electron approximation is assumed and therefore electron correlation is ignored.

Equation (45.1) cannot be expected to be true if the energy of the light is such as to cause autoionisation. For example, in Xe the $^2P_{1/2}$ and $^2P_{3/2}$ Rydberg limits lie at 13·432 eV and 12·126 eV, respectively, the channels being,

$$Xe(5p^6, {}^1S_0) \rightarrow Xe^+(5p^5, {}^2P_{1/2})ns$$

$$Xe(5p^6, {}^1S_0) \rightarrow Xe^+(5p^5, {}^2P_{1/2})nd, \text{ etc.}$$

The last few lines of the above lie within the $^2P_{3/2}$ continuum and are therefore susceptible to autoionisation. In the region between the two ionisation limits the asymmetry parameter is found to change rapidly with the light energy (figure 45.2).

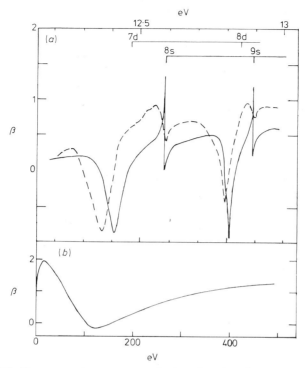

Figure 45.2. The asymmetry parameter, β, plotted against light energy for the ionisation of the $5p^6$ subshell of xenon. (*a*) Full curve, theoretical, calculated from angular momentum considerations (Dill 1973); broken curve, experimental (Samson and Gardner 1973). Note the sharp changes in the theoretical curve due to autoionisation at the energies of the ns Rydberg levels; these structures are too sharp for a complete experimental resolution. (*b*) Theoretical (Manson 1973), based on the Hartree–Slater model of the atom. In the absence of autoionisation, at the higher energies, the curve is free of rapid changes.

46 Angular Distribution in O_2

The nature of the first band in the spectrum of O_2 was discussed in § 43, and the threshold lies at about 12 eV. In the absorption spectrum of O_2 there is a Rydberg series converging on the $^4\Sigma_g^-$ state of the ion. The terms of the series are given by

$$h\nu = R\left[1{\cdot}336 - \frac{1}{(n-0{\cdot}68)^2}\right].$$

Terms are recorded for the values $n = 4, 5 \ldots 16$. The ionisation threshold of the $^4\Sigma_g^-$ state is evidently at about $18{\cdot}16$ eV. If, in taking the photelectron spectrum, the ionising radiation used happens to be the $16{\cdot}85$ eV line of neon, the first term of the above Rydberg series lies quite close in energy to it at $16{\cdot}93$ eV, and there will a component of the Rydberg state in the molecular state existing immediately after the interaction with the photon has occurred. In other words, the direct photoelectric effect will be complicated by the presence of autoionisation.

The use of He 21·21 eV radiation involves no such complication, and gives a spectrum in which the $^2\Pi_g$ band has four prominent vibrational components (figure 49.1). If the neon line is employed, however, ten additional vibrational peaks appear (figure 46.1). These extra peaks have gained intensity from the Rydberg component of the intermediate wavefunction.

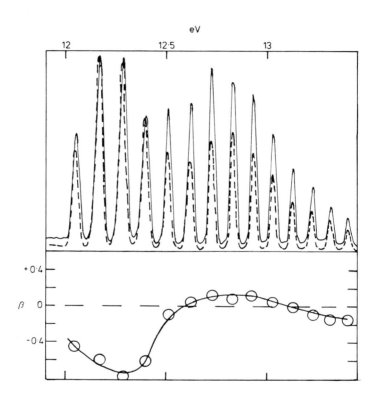

Figure 46.1. Photoelectron spectra of O_2 taken with Ne resonance radiation (16·85 eV). The angle between the propagation direction of the light beam and the photoelectrons was 20° for the broken curve, and 90° for the full curve. The spectra are arbitrarily normalised so that the peaks of greatest intensity appear to have the same height. In the lower part of the figure the corresponding asymmetry parameter values are given (Carlson 1971); after the fourth peak the emission is not far from isotropic.

In figure 46.1 there are two photoelectron spectra of O_2; in one the angle between the direction of the light beam and the photoelectrons is 20° and in the other it is 90°. From the differences in the two spectra the β values were determined (equation (44.3)), and they are plotted in the lower part of the figure. It is noteworthy that the value of β is close to zero after the fourth peak, indicating that the lifetime of the autoionising state is sufficiently long to allow rotation of the molecule before photoemission.

Problems

1 Show that for the operator er^2, equation (44.2) becomes

$$p = A \cos^4 \theta + B \cos^2 \theta + C.$$

This is the angular dependence law for electric quadrupole transitions. Find the condition for which the emission probability is independent of θ.

2 In the first band of N_2 ($^2\Sigma_g^+$), there are two vibrational components, the first having the value $\beta = 0.68$ and the second having $\beta = 1.5$. Plot the ratio of the intensities of the two peaks against both the angle between the electric vector and the escape vector of the photoelectron (equation (44.2)), and against the angle between the direction of the light beam and the escape vector (equation (44.3)). What is the best measurement to make, from the experimental point of view, in order to measure β, remembering that the electron detector cannot lie in the beam?

6 Diatomic Molecules

47 Carbon Monoxide

The spectra of CO, N_2 and O_2 have been carefully measured in Samson's labora-tory (see Gardner and Samson 1973), with the angle between the light beam and the photoelectron equal to $54° 44'$ (§ 44). Additionally, the ionising radiation was passed through a monochromator set for the He $40·8$ eV line and excluding the $23·08$ and $21·21$ eV lines. Although the experimental arrangement produced a very pure ionising radiation, it was also weak in intensity, and a period of four or five days was necessary to accumulate a spectrum with sufficient intensity.

Four peaks appear in the spectrum of CO (figure 47.1). Since first peak is sharp, it is attributed to the ionisation of a non-bonding orbital (labelled 5σ in figure 47.1) and is calculated to have the lowest energy eigenvalue of the set (Cambray *et al* 1974). As in the case of O_2 (§ 46), the use of $16·85$ eV ionising radiation produces a spectrum in which the vibrational structure of the first band is considerably extended. Under these conditions the structure of the 5σ peak extends as far as the second peak in the 1π band (Gardner and Samson 1974). In the optical spectrum of CO there is no structure around $16·85$ eV, but only the ionisation continuum can be found, so it is likely that the lifetime of the autoionising states is so short that the structure has become broad enough to merge with the continuum. The asymmetry parameters for He(II) radiation of the two vibrational peaks of the 5σ band are $0·95$ ($n = 0$) and $0·56$ ($n = 1$) (Hancock and Samson 1976).

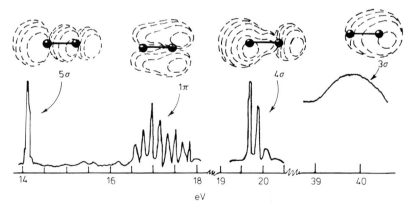

Figure 47.1. The photoelectron spectrum of CO (Gardner and Samson 1973) showing the electron density contours of the molecular orbitals corresponding to the peaks (Jorgensen and Salem 1973). The nuclear skeleton is drawn as a dumb-bell, where the oxygen atom lies on the right. Under conditions of high resolution, the 1π band is found to consist of twin peaks separated $0·0146$ eV by spin–orbit interaction.

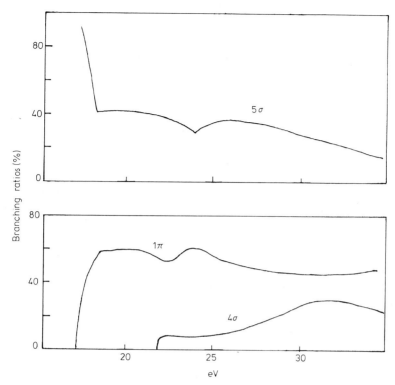

Figure 47.2. Branching ratios for the photoelectron spectrum of CO plotted against light energy (Samson and Gardner 1976).

Assignment of the remainder of the bands of CO is straightforward. As can be seen from figure 47.1, the orbitals of the remaining bands are all bonding, although the absence of structure on the 3σ band is indicative of predissociation. The relative intensities of the bands or 'branching ratios' are found to vary with the energy of the ionising radiation (figure 47.2). Average values of β for He(II) radiation are $0\cdot31$ (1π) and $0\cdot28$ (4σ) (Hancock and Samson 1976).

48 The Nitrogen Molecule

As in CO, the first band of N_2 is clearly the ionisation of a non-bonding orbital. N_2 and CO are isoelectronic and in both molecules the orbital of lowest ionisation energy is the 5σ of figure 47.1, but it is labelled $3\sigma_g^+$ in N_2 (figure 48.1), the symmetry having changed from $C_{\infty v}$ to $D_{\infty h}$ (table 48.1). The vibrational structure of the first band in N_2, as in CO and O_2, is enhanced by autoionisation if $16\cdot85$ eV light is used instead of $21\cdot21$ eV light. The second peak of N_2 corresponds with the second peak of CO. Again, the peaks marked $2\sigma_u^+$ and $2\sigma_g^+$ in figure 48.1 are assigned by comparison with the peaks of CO.

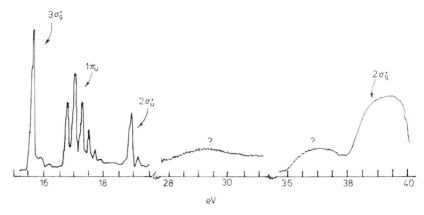

Figure 48.1. The photoelectron spectrum of molecular nitrogen (Gardner and Samson 1973). Monochromatic light of 40·77 eV was used, and the collecting angle of the photoelectrons was 54° 44′. The peaks with question marks are possibly two-electron transitions.

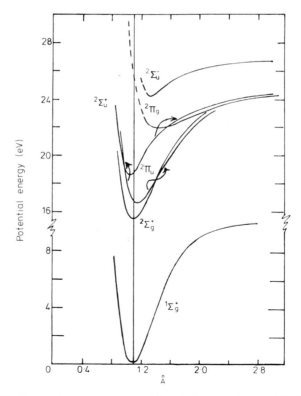

Figure 48.2. Potential energy curves for N_2^+ and the ground state of N_2 (Gilmore 1965). The broken curves are extrapolations of Gilmore's curves. Note the non-bonding nature of the $3\sigma_g^+$ orbital whose ionisation gives the state labelled $^2\Sigma_g^+$ in the diagram. Both $^2\Pi_g$ and $^2\Sigma_u^-$ are repulsive.

Table 48.1.

$D_{\infty h}$	E	$2C_\infty^\phi$	$\infty\sigma_v$	i	$2S_\infty^\phi$	$\infty C_2'$	
$\Sigma_g^+ = A_{1g}$	1	1	1	1	1	1	$z^2, x^2 + y^2$
$\Sigma_g^- = A_{2g}$	1	1	-1	1	1	-1	R_z
$\Pi_g = E_{1g}$	2	$2\cos\phi$	0	2	$-2\cos\phi$	0	R_x, R_y, xz, yz
$\Delta_g = E_{2g}$	2	$2\cos 2\phi$	0	2	$2\cos 2\phi$	0	$x^2 - y^2, xy$
. . .							
$\Sigma_u^+ = A_{1u}$	1	1	1	-1	-1	-1	z
$\Sigma_u^- = A_{2u}$	1	1	-1	-1	-1	1	
$\Pi_u = E_{1u}$	2	$2\cos\phi$	0	-2	$2\cos\phi$	0	x, y
$\Delta_u = E_{2u}$	2	$2\cos 2\phi$	0	-2	$-2\cos 2\phi$	0	
. . .							

The weak and broad features at 29 and 37 eV remain to be assigned. These may possibly arise from two-electron transitions in which the photoejection of one electron is accompanied by the promotion of another to an unoccupied orbital. The band at 37 eV may possibly be a two-electron transition in which both electrons are lost from $3\sigma_g^+$: one electron enters the antibonding $1\pi_g$ orbital and the other is ejected. The potential energy curve for the resultant $^2\Pi_g$ state is given in figure 48.2; its repulsive nature accounts for the lack of vibrational structure.

The band at 37 eV could possibly be due to a two-electron transition in which an electron is lost from both $3\sigma_g^+$ and $1\pi_u$, one entering $1\pi_g$ and the other being lost. The states arising from this transition have the symmetries of the direct product,

$$\Pi_u \times \Pi_g = \Sigma_g^+ = \Sigma_u^+ + \Sigma_u^- + \Delta_u.$$

The potential energy curve for the $^2\Sigma_u^-$ member of this set, so far as it is known, is given in figure 48.2.

49 The Oxygen Molecule

The electronic configuration of O_2 has already been discussed (§ 43), and it differs from that of N_2 in the outermost orbital, where O_2 has an extra pair of electrons in $1\pi_g$. The lowest ionisation energy results from the ionisation of $1\pi_g$ (§ 46).

The next in energy is $1\pi_u$, its ionisation giving rise to the states $^2\Pi_u \times {}^3\Sigma_g^- = {}^{2,4}\Pi_u$. Following this ionisation, we have the loss of an electron from $3\sigma_g^+$, giving the states $^{2,4}\Sigma_g^-$. All of the above states are represented in the spectrum, but of those arising from the ionisation of the next orbital, $2\sigma_u^+$, only $^4\Sigma_u^-$ can be found in figure 49.1. The spectrum in this figure was obtained using light of 40·8 eV energy, but the spectrum obtained with x-radiation does possess a peak attributable to the missing $^2\Sigma_u^-$ state at 27·9 eV. It is possible that the background of scattered electrons obtained with 40·8 eV radiation obscures the rather weak $^2\Sigma_u^-$ band. Peaks labelled $^{2,4}\Sigma_g^-$ in figure 49.1 arise from the ionisation of $2\sigma_g^+$.

Another peak at 23·6 eV, labelled $^2\Pi_u$, has been attributed (Gardner and Samson 1973) to the two-electron process consisting of the ionisation of $1\pi_u$, plus a simultaneous rearrangement of the outermost electrons. The following comple-

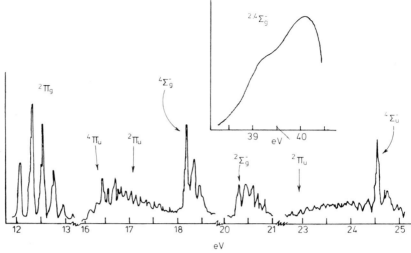

Figure 49.1. The photoelectron spectrum of O_2 (Gardner and Samson 1973) taken under the same conditions as the spectrum in figure 48.1.

ment of states results:

$$\Pi_u \times {}^1\Sigma_g^+ = {}^2\Pi_u \tag{49.1}$$

$$\Pi_u \times {}^3\Sigma_g^- = {}^{2,4}\Pi_u \tag{49.2}$$

$$\Pi_u \times {}^1\Delta_g = {}^2\Pi_u + {}^2\Phi_u. \tag{49.3}$$

Of these, only equation (49.2) arises from a one-electron transition, while the others involve a transition in the outermost orbital in addition to the photoemission. The forbidden nature of two-electron transitions arises because the transition dipole moment operator er is a one-electron operator. Hence an integral of the form $\langle \phi_1 \phi_2 | er | \phi_3 \phi_4 \rangle$ can be factorised as $\langle \phi_1 | er | \phi_3 \rangle \langle \phi_2 | \phi_4 \rangle$. The last term is zero because of the orthogonality of ϕ_2 and ϕ_4. However, there are reasons why the above expression is inadequate to explain the intensity in every case, particularly when it has a low value. For example, there is the possibility of electric quadrupole, rather than electric dipole, interaction between the molecule and the light, the relevant operator being er^2. In O_2, it is likely that mixing of the ${}^2\Pi_u$ states of equations (49.1)–(49.3) takes place (Dixon and Hull 1969). The component of allowed ${}^2\Pi_u$ character from equation (49.2) confers a finite transition moment upon transitions to ${}^2\Pi_u$ nominally derived from equations (49.1) and (49.3). In addition to the peak at 23·6 eV, a third ${}^2\Pi_u$ peak is anticipated, but its energy is expected to be larger. Since a large separation in energy between mixing states reduces the amount of mixing, it is plausible that the third peak is absent on account of its having only a small component of allowed one-electron character, and hence it is not seen in the spectrum.

Passage of O_2 through a microwave discharge produces a few per cent of O_2 (${}^1\Delta_g$) as a transient species. The photoelectron spectrum of O_2 in this state has been measured (Jonathan *et al* 1974), showing the expected ${}^2\Delta_g$ and ${}^2\Phi_u$ peaks.

50   Nitric Oxide, NO

The spectrum of NO is complicated by the overlapping of many bands (figure 50.1). The ground state is a doublet, there being one electron lesss than in O_2; calculated energies (in eV) are $-9\cdot14\,(2\pi)$, $-14\cdot61\,(5\sigma)$, $-15\cdot22\,(1\pi)$, $-23\cdot28\,(4\sigma)$, and $-40\cdot35\,(3\sigma)$ (Jorgensen and Salem 1973).

Ionisation of 2π gives the $^1\Sigma^+$ state at the energy expected by Koopmans' theorem, without overlapping by other peaks. This first band in the spectrum resembles the first band of O_2 in a number of ways: for example, the vibrational progression is extended by replacing He resonance radiation by Ar radiation (Caprace *et al* 1976), which is a consequence of autoionisation. The vibrational interval of $0\cdot28$ eV exceeds the frequency for the neutral molecule ($0\cdot234$ eV); this is evidence of the antibonding nature of the outermost orbital. The bond length is $1\cdot16$ Å in the neutral molecule and about $1\cdot07$ Å in the $^1\Sigma^+$ state (Gilmore 1965).

The loss of a 5σ electron gives $^{1,3}\Pi$ states. Since the orbital is non-bonding the peaks are expected to be sharp (compare figure 59.1) and they are found at $16\cdot5$ and $18\cdot3$ eV. According to Lindholm (see Edqvist *et al* 1971) the $^{1,3}\Pi$ states from the ionisation of 4σ both lie near $21\cdot7$ eV. The triplet has three times the intensity of the singlet, and is attributed to the sharp peak at $21\cdot7$ eV; the singlet is broader and lies at slightly higher energy.

Six states derive from the ionisation of 1π, namely, $^{1,3}(\Delta, \Sigma^+, \Sigma^-)$, all of which have been assigned by Lindholm and co-workers on grounds of intensity, vibrational structure, comparison with CO and N_2, and calculated ionisation energy (Edqvist *et al* 1971). Using Mg Kα radiation, Siegbahn *et al* (1969) have found two peaks at $40\cdot6$ and $43\cdot8$ eV, and have ascribed these to the ionisation of 3σ.

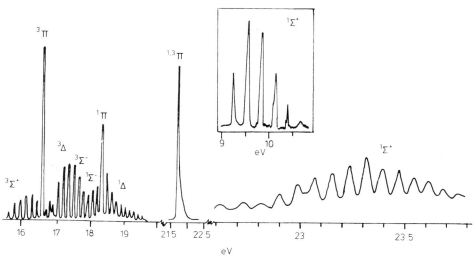

Figure 50.1. The photoelectron spectrum of nitric oxide, NO. Inset, the first band, taken with $21\cdot21$ eV radiation (Turner *et al* 1970). The rest of the spectrum was obtained with $40\cdot77$ eV radiation (Edqvist *et al* 1971).

51 The Halogens

In order of increasing ionisation energy, the first orbitals of the halogens are $1\pi_g$, $1\pi_u$ and $2\sigma_g$ (figure 51.1).

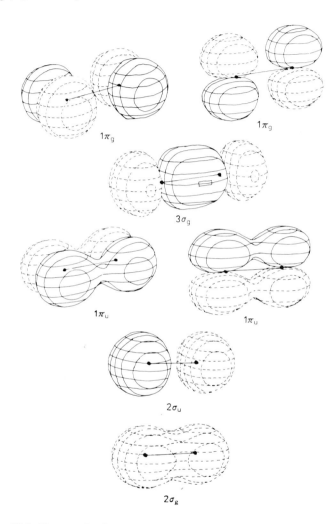

Figure 51.1. Electron density contours of the occupied orbitals of F_2 (Jorgensen and Salem 1973).

Since $1\pi_g$ is an antibonding orbital, the loss of an electron from it causes a decrease in the bond length of about $0 \cdot 1$ Å (Potts *et al* 1970), and a slight increase in the vibrational frequency. There is a splitting of the first band as a result of spin–orbit interaction; the magnitudes of the energy separations of the components are close to the magnitudes of the one-electron spin–orbit coupling constants.

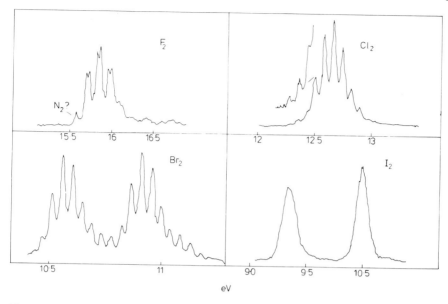

Figure 51.2. The first bands in the photoelectron spectra of the halogens (Potts and Price 1971) obtained with light of 21·21 eV energy, except for Br_2, where 16·8 eV was used.

There is an interesting sequence of changes in the structure of the first bands of the halogens as the atomic number rises and the spin–orbit parameter increases in magnitude. At first, in F_2, the spin–orbit interaction splits every vibrational peak; in Cl_2 the vibrational interval and the spin–orbit splitting have the same magnitude, and the structure appears to consist of a simple vibrational progression of overlapping peaks (figure 51.2). In Br_2 the spin–orbit splitting is much larger than the vibrational interval and both spin–orbit components have a well developed vibrational progression. The same would be true of I_2 but the vibrational structure is lost, possibly due to the population of vibrational states of the neutral molecule.

The second band is broader and, except in I_2, the spin–orbit peaks are not distinctly separated. In I_2 the splitting is 0·8 eV in $1\pi_u$ and 0·65 eV in $1\pi_g$.

Problems

1 Predict the spectra of SiO and B_2. Why are these molecules unstable?

2 Derive the states arising from the ionisation of O_2 in its $^1\Sigma_g^+$ and $^1\Delta_g$ states.

3 By heating the white solid P_3N_5, a vapour believed to be PN was obtained. The He(I) spectrum of the vapour possessed a sharp line at 11·85 eV and a broad band with three vibrational peaks at 12·34 eV. The remainder of the spectrum was weak and overlapped by impurity bands. Assign the first two bands to states of the PN^+ ion.

4 In the spectrum of ICl the first two bands have the adiabatic ionisation energies 9·80 and 10·45 eV. Fine structure is found in the form of peaks at 9·98, 10·03, 10·08, 10·13, 10·18 and 10·23 eV on the first band, and 10·62, 10·67, 10·72, 10·77, 10·82 and 10·87 eV on the second. Suggest an explanation for the fine structure and assign the bands to states of ICl⁺.

7 Molecules Related to Ethylene

52 Acetylene, Ethylene and Ethane

Acetylene, ethylene and ethane contain 10, 12 and 14 valence electrons, respectively, are isoelectronic with N_2, O_2 and F_2 and, like the latter, they comprise a series in which the central linkage is progressively weakened. Along the series the C—C bond length increases (1·21, 1·33 and 1·55 Å, respectively), and the heats of dissociation decrease (8·7, 6·3 and 3·6 eV, respectively). In § 30 the spectrum of acetylene was discussed in relation to the spectra of other linear molecules. In figures 52.1 and 52.2 the ionisation energies and orbitals of acetylene are correlated with those of ethylene and ethane.

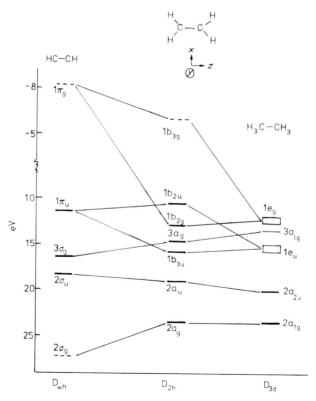

Figure 52.1. Ionisation energies of acetylene, ethylene and ethane showing how the molecular orbitals are correlated. Broken lines indicate values calculated by Koopmans' theorem, but not observed, either because the orbital is not occupied or the corresponding peak was not identified in the spectrum.

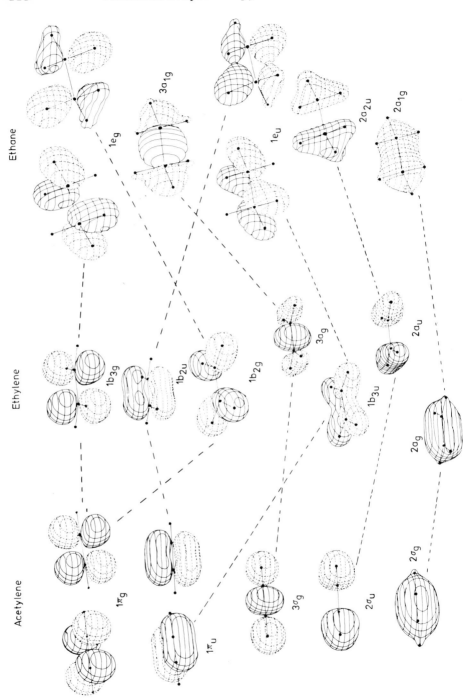

Figure 52.2. Molecular orbital correlation diagram showing the electron density contours of acetylene, ethylene and ethane (Jorgensen and Salem 1973).

Rotation about the C—C bond is of some interest in this series. In acetylene such a rotation has no apparent meaning, but in ethane the frequency of the torsional vibration has been measured and corresponds to only 0.034 eV, compared with between 0.087 and 0.099 eV in ethylene. In ethylene, therefore, there is a large resistance to forces tending to make the molecule non-planar, and this can be attributed to the occupation of the $1b_{2g}$ orbital (figure 52.2). When the CH_2 planes of ethylene are perpendicular to each other, the $1b_{2g}$ and the $1b_{3g}$ orbitals are degenerate and the Jahn–Teller theorem would lead us to expect such a geometry to be unstable. In ethane the occupation of the orbital deriving from $1b_{3g}$ in ethylene reduces the constraint upon rotation. The geometry of ethane is staggered (figure 52.2), that is, it has the maximum distance between the protons. The barrier to rotation of the CH_3 groups is 0.127 eV, and SCF calculations indicate that about two-thirds of this energy is due to the $1e_g$ orbitals (Topiol and Ratner 1977).

As a rule, the more saturated the hydrocarbon the more diffuse is its spectrum and there is some uncertainty regarding the assignment of the bands in the spectrum of ethylene, for example, with respect to the relative positions of the $3a_g$ and

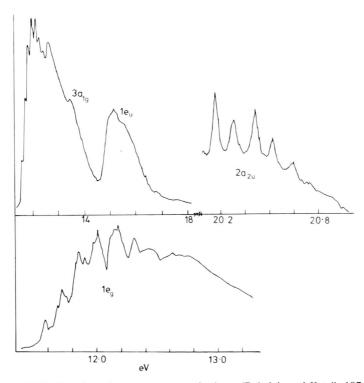

Figure 52.3. The photoelectron spectrum of ethane (Rabalais and Katrib 1974), using light of energy 21.21 eV. The lower spectrum is an expansion of the $1e_g$ region.

the $1b_{2g}$ ionisations (Turner *et al* 1970). The spectrum of ethane is particularly crowded in the low-energy region between 11·8 and 14 eV (figure 52.3), and there is an irregular vibrational progression with many small peaks and shoulders which are suggestive of Jahn–Teller splitting.

A further complication in the spectrum of ethane is the dissociation

$$C_2H_6 = CH_3^+ + CH_3 \cdot + e^-$$

which occurs at 13·6 eV. The loss of an electron from the C—C bonding $3a_{1g}$ orbital probably causes the above dissociation, since the ionisation energy appears to be about 13·5 eV and a broad, structureless band results.

53   Diborane, B_2H_6

Diborane melts at $-165\cdot5\,°C$ and boils at $-92\cdot5\,°C$; it is a stable compound but it is hydrolysed by water. If the SCF energies of diborane are reduced by the empirical factor of 0·92, Koopmans' theorem is found to hold moderately well (table 53.1), and this factor of 0·92 also applies to a number of other compounds containing first-row elements.

Table 53.1. Observed and calculated ionisation energies of B_2H_6 (Brundle *et al* 1970a).

	Peak maximum (eV)	SCF eigenvalue $\times 0\cdot92$
$1b_{2u}$	14·7	$-13\cdot8$
$1b_{2g}$	11·81	$-11\cdot6$
$3a_g$	13·3	$-12\cdot9$
$1b_{3u}$	13·9	$-13\cdot4$
$1b_{1u}$	16·06	$-16\cdot00$
$2a_g$	21·4	$-22\cdot3$

Diborane is isoelectronic with ethylene and can be regarded as deriving from it by the withdrawal of a proton from each carbon atom to a position vertically above the molecular plane (figure 53.1). The B–B separation of 1·77 Å is marginally longer than the sum of the covalent radii (1·6 Å), but this is such a small difference that the boron atoms are evidently in contact. The molecular orbital of ethylene most affected by proton withdrawal is naturally expected to be that with most electronic density in the region to which the protons are withdrawn. This orbital is $1b_{2u}$ and its energy is greatly lowered by proton displacement, which accounts for the stability of the molecule.

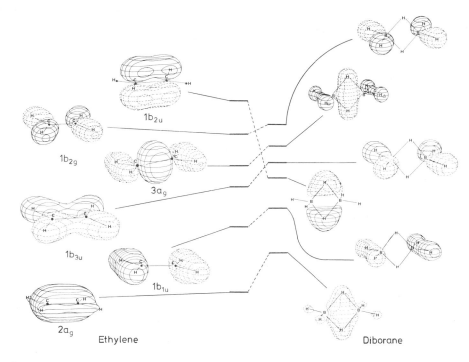

Figure 53.1. Correlation of the orbitals of ethylene and diborane. The horizontal bars represent ionisation energies. The most important difference between the molecules is the change in the energy of the $1b_{2u}$ orbital possesses high electronic density in diborane at the position of the bridging hydrogen atoms.

54   Ethylene Glycol, $(CH_2OH)_2$

For a large molecule the spectrum of ethylene glycol is unusually well resolved; all nine of the bands accessible to He(I) radiation are visible (figure 54.1). These bands arise from the six H(1s) electrons plus the twelve 2p electrons of carbon and oxygen. Assignment of the bands follows from a consideration of the spectra of methanol (which in turn derives from that of water) and ethane. Figure 54.2 is a correlation diagram for these spectra.

The orbitals corresponding to $1b_1$ and the $3a_1$ of H_2O are more easily ionised in methanol, where they become $2a''$ and $7a'$ (point group C_s). The $1b_2$ orbital of H_2O is also subject to a lowering of ionisation energy in methanol, where it becomes the $6a'$ orbital and mixes a good deal with the orbitals of the $.CH_3$ component. In the spectrum of ethylene glycol the four orbitals derived from $2a''$ and $7a'$ of methanol are evident at the lower ionisation end; splitting of the associated bands can be expected from the in-phase and out-of-phase combinations of the pairs of methanol orbitals (table 54.1).

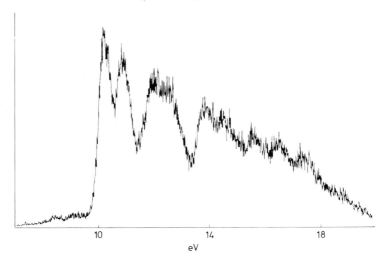

Figure 54.1. The photoelectron spectrum of ethylene glycol obtained using He(I) radiation.

The remaining five bands of figure 54.1 come mainly from the combination of the orbitals of .CH_2CH_2. with those derived from $1b_2$ of H_2O. They can be regarded as the upper five bands of ethane (figure 52.1) perturbed by the substitution of C—OH for C—H at two positions. This substitution greatly raises their ionisation energies.

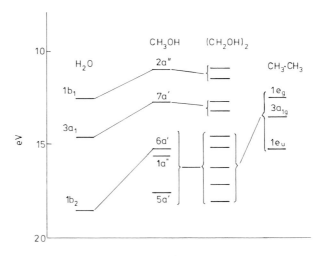

Figure 54.2. Correlation diagram for the observed ionisation energies of ethylene glycol and related molecules.

Table 54.1. Observed and calculated ionisation energies of ethylene glycol (C_{2h} symmetry is assumed).

	Peak maximum (eV)	SCF eigenvalue $\times 0.92$
$2b_g$	10·6	11·09
$2a_u$	11·29	11·50
$7a_g$	12·52	11·89
$6b_u$	13.00	13.08
$6a_g$	14·41	14·54
$1b_g$	15·11	14·94
$5a_g$	16·13	16·61
$1a_u$	17·08	17·16
$5b_u$	18·01	17·78

55 Butadiene and Hexatriene

The photoelectron spectra of *cis*- and *trans*-1,3,5-hexatriene are very similar, even with regard to their vibrational structure (figure 55.1). This observation encourages the belief that the neglect of non-nearest-neighbour interactions, as in the simplest Hückel theory (§ 18), will not go too far amiss here (this would not be the case with the tetrahedral molecules of Chapter 9).

The pi orbitals of butadiene (figure 55.2) can be regarded as the in-phase and the out-of-phase combinations of the $1b_{2u}$ orbital of ethylene (figure 52.2). They can be written

$$\pi_{+,-} = (1/\sqrt{2})(\pi_a \pm \pi_b) \qquad (55.1)$$

where π_a is the ethylenic $1b_{2u}$ orbital on one half of the molecule, and π_b is on the other. Although the components are molecular orbitals there is no difference in principle between the above and equation (18.1), where atomic orbitals are involved. The advantage of expressing the wavefunction in this manner is that the known ionisation energy of the ethylene orbital, 10·51 eV, can be used in the calculation. Thus

$$\langle \pi_a | H | \pi_a \rangle = H_{aa} = -10·51 \text{ eV}.$$

Applying simple Hückel theory (§ 18) the energies of the butadiene orbitals are

$$E_{+,-} = H_{aa} \pm H_{ab}.$$

Equating these energies with the values observed in butadiene (table 55.1) for the ionisation of the pi orbitals, we derive that $H_{ab} = -1·22$ eV and $H_{aa} = -10·25$ eV. It appears that the linkage of one ethylenic residue to another causes a change in the

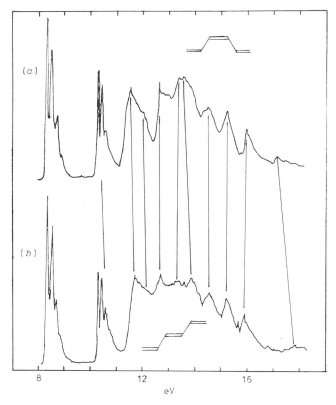

Figure 55.1. The photoelectron spectra of (*a*) *cis*-1,3,5-hexatriene, and (*b*) *trans*-1,3,5-hexatriene (Beez *et al* 1973). The spectra are remarkably similar.

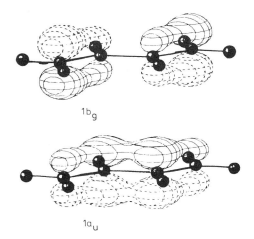

Figure 55.2. The occupied molecular orbitals of pi symmetry in *trans*-butadiene (Jorgensen and Salem 1973). The upper orbital, $1b_g$, has the wavefunction with the negative sign in equation (55.1), and the lower orbital, $1a_u$, takes the positive sign.

Table 55.1. Ionisation energies, I, and calculated orbital energies, E (SCF) for 1,3-butadiene, *cis*- and *trans*-1,3,5-hexatriene, in eV (Beez *et al* 1973).

Butadiene (C_{2h})			cis-hexatriene (C_{2v})			trans-hexatriene (C_{2h})		
	I	$-E$		I	$-E$		I	$-E$
$1b_g(\pi)$	9·03	9·41	$2b_1(\pi)$	8·32	8·88	$2a_u(\pi)$	8·29	8·89
$1a_u(\pi)$	11·46	11·40	$1a_2(\pi)$	10·27	10·51	$1b_g(\pi)$	10·26	10·55
$7a_g$	12·23	11·89	$9b_2$	11·5	11·43	$10a_g$	11·6	11·86
$6b_u$	13·0	12·91	$1b_1(\pi)$	~11·9	11·81	$1a_u(\pi)$	~11·9	11·81
$6a_g$	13·3	13·44	$10a_1$	12·6	12·61	$9b_u$	12·6	12·23
$5a_g$	15·3	15·33	$9a_1$	13·4	13·18	$9a_g$	13·3	12·93
$5b_u$	?	15·42	$8b_2$	13·5	13·38	$8a_g$	13·9	13·58
$4b_u$	17·9	17·87	$7b_2$	14·5	14·29	$8b_u$	14·5	14·38
			$8a_1$	15·2	15·17	$7b_u$	15·2	15·18
			$7a_1$	16·0	16·29	$7a_g$	15·9	16·12
			$6b_2$	17·2	16·98	$6a_g$	17·8	17·60

value of H_{aa} of 0·26 eV. Two such linkages, as in the middle residue of hexatriene, presumably cause a further fall of 0·26 eV, with the result that H_{aa} takes the value of $-9·99$ eV. The resulting secular determinant is

$$\begin{vmatrix} (-10·25-E) & (-1·22) & 0 \\ (-1·22) & (-9·99-E) & (-1·22) \\ 0 & (-1·22) & (-10·25-E) \end{vmatrix} = 0$$

with the solutions $E = -8·39$, $-10·25$ and $-11·85$ eV. These are the energies of the first three pi orbitals in hexatriene. They compare well with the observed ionisation energies given in table 55.1. Using the ethylene $1b_{2g}$ orbital, it is possible to calculate the first three sigma ionisation energies of hexatriene in the same way.

56   Inner Valence Orbitals of the Alkanes

In the higher alkanes, the region of the spectrum below 18 eV is crowded with overlapping bands. The flexible nature of these compounds leads to the presence of a range of molecular conformations; consequently, the bands are broad and the problem of resolving them is worsened. That part of the spectrum lying between 18 and 27 eV is relatively well resolved, however, and assignments can be made without difficulty (table 56.1).

The orbital of methane which undergoes ionisation in this region, $2a_1$, is largely of C(2s) parentage (figure 17.2) with H(1s) and a little C(1s). It will be assumed that this orbital can be used to make up molecular orbitals of the higher alkanes in the same manner as the ethylenic orbitals were used in § 55 to make up butadiene and hexatriene. To simplify matters further, the same Coulomb integral, H_{aa}, and the same resonance integral, H_{ab} can be used throughout. With this approximation, the

Table 56.1. Ionisation energies (in eV) for the inner valence shells of the alkanes (Potts and Streets 1974).

		Straight chain
(T_d)	CH_4	$22 \cdot 91$ $(1a_1)$
$(D_{\infty h})$	C_2H_6	$23 \cdot 9$ $(1\sigma_g)$; $20 \cdot 42$ $(1\sigma_u)$
(C_{2v})	C_3H_8	$24 \cdot 5$ $(1a_1)$; $22 \cdot 1$ $(1b_2)$; $19 \cdot 15$ $(2a_1)$
(C_{2h})	$CH_3(CH_2)_2CH_3$	$24 \cdot 7$ $(1a_g)$; 23 $(1b_u)$; $20 \cdot 7$ $(2a_g)$; $18 \cdot 8$ $(2b_u)$
(C_{2v})	$CH_3(CH_2)_3CH_3$	$24 \cdot 8$ $(1a_1)$; $23 \cdot 7$ $(1b_2)$; $21 \cdot 7$ $(2a_1)$; $19 \cdot 9$ $(2b_2)$; $18 \cdot 74$ $(2b_u)$

	Cyclic $(CH_2)_n$, symmetry $D_{\infty h}$
$n = 3$	$26 \cdot 5$ $(1a_1')$; $19 \cdot 5$ $(1e')$
4	$?$ $(1a_{1g})$; 21 $(1e_u)$; $18 \cdot 25$ $(1b_{1g})$
5	$?(1a_1')$; $22 \cdot 2$ $(1e_1')$; $18 \cdot 29$ $(1e_2')$
6	$25 \cdot 7$ $(1a_{1g})$; $23 \cdot 1$ $(1e_{1u})$; $19 \cdot 49$ $(1e_{2g})$; $18 \cdot 06$ $(1b_{1u})$
7	$?(1a)$; $23 \cdot 7$ $(1e_1)$; $20 \cdot 55$ $(1e_2)$; $18 \cdot 07$ $(1e_3)$
8	$?(1a_1)$; $23 \cdot 9$ $(1e_1)$; $21 \cdot 4$ $(1e_2)$; $18 \cdot 75$ $(1e_3)$; $17 \cdot 66$ $(1b_2)$

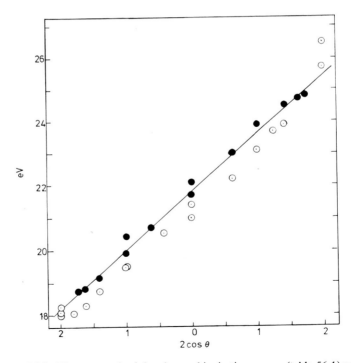

Figure 56.1. Alkanes; graph of the observed ionisation energy (table 56.1) against $2 \cos \theta$, where θ is either $j\pi/(n+1)$ or $2j\pi/(n+1)$ according to whether the molecule is cyclic or open-chain (equations (56.1) and (56.2)). Full circles refer to linear compounds and open circles refer to cyclic compounds.

Hückel energies in the linear case are given by (Coulson *et al* 1965)

$$E_j = H_{aa} + 2\cos\left(\frac{j\pi}{n+1}\right) H_{ab} \tag{56.1}$$

and in the cyclic case by

$$E_j = H_{aa} + 2\cos\left(\frac{2j\pi}{n}\right) H_{ab} \tag{56.2}$$

where n is the number of C atoms in the molecule and $j = 1, 2, 3, \ldots, n$.

In figure 56.1 the appropriate cosine term of equations (56.1) and (56.2) is plotted against the ionisation energy (table 56.1), and a straight-line plot is obtained.

By dropping the assumption that H_{aa} has a constant value and solving the determinants that result, a rather better straight line is found and the variation of the magnitude of H_{aa} with the number of attached H atoms can be explored. Values of H_{aa} so derived are $-22 \cdot 91$ eV (CH_4), $-22 \cdot 0$ eV (CH_3), $-21 \cdot 6$ eV (CH_2), $-21 \cdot 3$ eV (CH) and $-21 \cdot 0$ eV (C) (Potts and Streets 1974). It is concluded that the more C—H bonds there are, the more tightly bound the electrons become.

57 Benzene

The high symmetry of benzene (point group D_{6h}), coupled with the near degeneracy of some of the orbitals, produces difficulty in the interpretation of the spectrum. In particular, it has been difficult to decide whether the second band is due to the ionisation of $1a_{2u}$ (a pi orbital), or $3e_{2g}$ (a sigma orbital) (figure 57.1). The first band in the spectrum has a complex vibrational structure attributable to the Jahn–Teller effect; it is therefore doubly degenerate and is assigned to the ionisation of $1e_{1g}(\pi)$, in accordance with SCF calculations (table 57.1).

Regarding the second band, the evidence is conflicting. Calculations predict that the second ionisation is either that of $3e_{2g}(\sigma)$ or $1a_{2u}(\pi)$. Analysis of the vibrational

Table 57.1. Ionisation energies of benzene: SCF calculations (Schulman and Moskowitz 1967) and peak maxima (Åsbrink 1972).

	Calculated (eV)	Observed (eV)
$1e_{1g}(\pi)$	10·15	9·3
$3e_{2g}$	14·26	11·8
$1a_{2u}(\pi)$	14·56	12·5
$3e_{1u}$	16·92	14·0
$1b_{2u}$	17·80	14·9
$2b_{1u}$	18·01	15·5
$3a_{1g}$	20·08	17·0
$2e_{2g}$		19·2
$2e_{1u}$		22·7
$2a_{1g}$		25·8

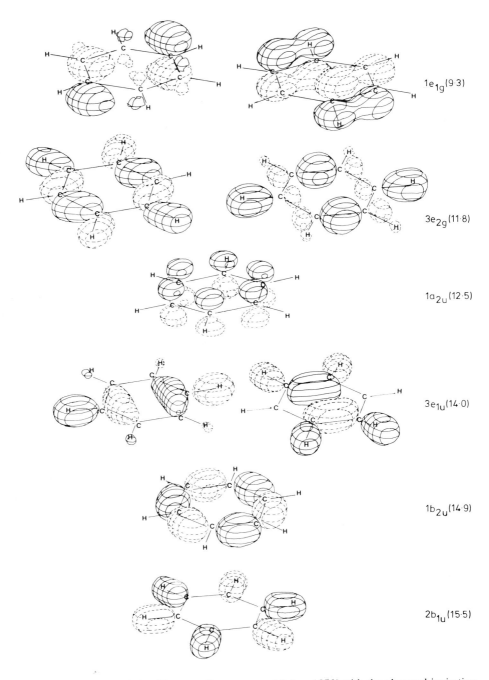

Figure 57.1. Molecular orbitals of benzene (Jorgensen and Salem 1973) with the observed ionisation energies (peak maxima; Åsbrink 1972). Symmetries are given for the D_{6h} point group.

structure has led to both assignments (Itah 1977). Studies of the effect of deu-teration have put the ionisation of $1a_{2u}$ in the second place (El-Sayed *et al* 1961), whilst studies of the effect of fluorination have put $3e_{2g}$ there (Narayan and Murrell 1970).

There are two Rydberg series in the optical spectrum of benzene which converge at 9·25 and 11·49 eV. The second of these corresponds to the second band in the photoelectron spectrum and has a similar vibrational structure (figure 57.2). It has been concluded that this second series terminates with the ionisation of the $3e_{2g}$ orbital (Itah 1977), and therefore that the $3e_{2g}$ ionisation is the second band in the photoelectron spectrum.

The asymmetry parameter changes on passing through the second band, sugges-ting degeneracy (Carlson 1971), whereas it changes little on passage through the third band. This again suggests that $3e_{2g}$ is the second and $1a_{2u}$ is the third band.

The ionisation energies of the pi orbitals can readily be calculated by the method of § 55. From figure 57.1 it can be seen that the $1e_{1g}$ orbital of benzene is made up of a pair of out-of-phase ethylene $1b_{2u}$ orbitals, separated by a nodal plane. The ionisation energy is therefore equal to $-H_{aa} = 9\cdot99$ eV. In Dewar benzene (figure 57.3) the same orbital ionises at 9·7 eV (Goldstein *et al* 1976). The $1a_{2u}$ orbital of benzene, on the other hand, is comprised of three ethylene $1b_{2u}$ orbitals arranged in-phase; using the values $H_{aa} = -9\cdot99$ and $H_{ab} = -1\cdot22$ eV, we obtain from equa-tion (56.2) the ionisation energy of 12·43 eV, compared with the observed energy of 12·5 eV.

The sandwich compound $(\pi\text{-}C_6H_6)_2Cr$ possesses all the benzene peaks, plus two extra peaks at 5·4 and 6·4 eV (Evans *et al* 1972a). The extra peaks are the result of

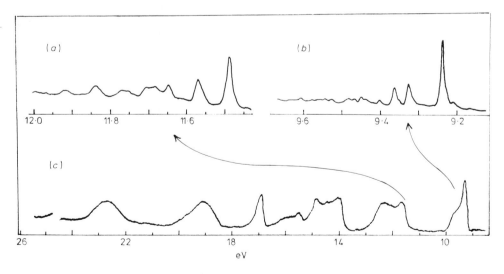

Figure 57.2. The photoelectron spectrum of benzene. (*c*) Spectrum obtained using light of energy 40·77 eV; (*a*) and (*b*) are expansions of the first and second bands of the spectrum using the 10·2 eV H line (Åsbrink *et al* 1970b).

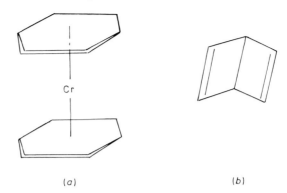

(a) (b)

Figure 57.3. The structure of (a) $(\pi\text{-}C_6H_6)_2Cr$ and (b) Dewar benzene.

the ionisation of the six valence electrons of Cr which occupy δ_g and σ_g^+ orbitals if it is assumed that the symmetry is $D_{\infty h}$, that is, if free rotation of the benzene molecules is assumed.

58 Pyridine and Pyrazine

Pyridine and pyrazine are slightly basic, strongly smelling substances derived from benzene by the substitution of respectively one and two C—H groups by nitrogen atoms. In pyrazine the nitrogen atoms are in the *para* positions. Because N and CH are isoelectronic no new bands are created by the substitution, but certain changes in energy result. It is helpful to ascribe two simple reasons for these changes, namely, the loss of the proton of the CH bond from the position of the H atom and the increase in electronegativity at the position of substitution.

The consequence of the loss of the proton of the CH bond is a decrease in ionisation energy for any orbital having a C—H bonding lobe at the position of substitution. For example, the C—H bond furthest to the right of the pair labelled $3e_{2g}$ in figure 57.1 has such a lobe extending along it. On the other hand, this is not the case with $1e_{1g}$, nor for any other pi molecular orbital because they all have a node in the molecular plane.

The change in ionisation energy which results from the change in electronegativity at the position of substitution is approximately given by

$$\Delta E = -c^2 \Delta(H_{aa}) \tag{58.1}$$

where $\Delta(H_{aa})$ is the change in the Coulomb integral at the position of substitution (about $-4\,eV$ in this case), and c is the atomic orbital coefficient at this position.

In figure 58.1 the coefficients of the Hückel pi orbitals of benzene are set out. Using equation (58.1) it is now possible to calculate how the orbital ionisation energies will be affected by the N-substitution of the CH groups. The choice of the position of substitution of the first CH group (to give pyridine) makes no difference to the calculation, but it is convenient to choose a position lying on a nodal plane of

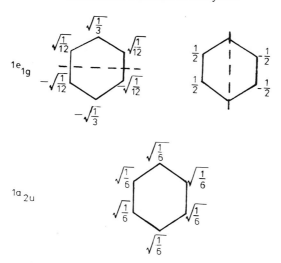

Figure 58.1. The Hückel orbital coefficients of the occupied pi molecular orbitals of benzene.

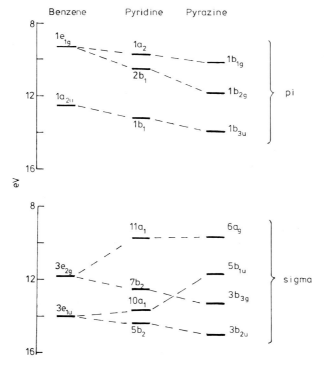

Figure 58.2. Ionisation energies of the upper orbitals of benzene, pyridine and pyrazine. The assignments and correlations are tentative. The point group of pyrazine is D_{2h}, and that of pyridine is C_{2v}.

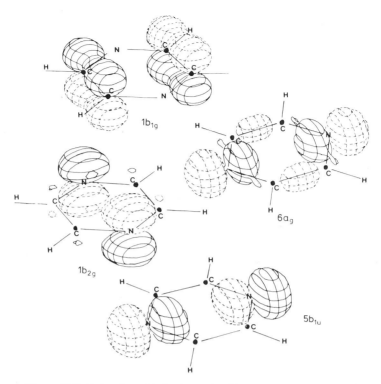

Figure 58.3. Molecular orbitals of pyrazine (Jorgensen and Salem 1973).

one of the orbitals of a degenerate pair. Such a choice enables one to see at once that the substitution causes no change in the ionisation energy of the orbital with a nodal plane at the position of substitution, whereas the other orbital does suffer a change. For example, the left-hand $1e_{1g}$ orbital of figure 58.1 increases in energy by $\frac{1}{3}\Delta(H_{aa})$ or $\frac{4}{3}$ eV (figure 58.2). Thus in pyridine it is expected that the degeneracy of the benzenoid $1e_{1g}$ orbital will be lifted, one orbital remaining at the same ionisation energy and the other increasing in ionisation energy by approximately $\frac{4}{3}$ eV. In pyrazine, it is anticipated that the energy gap between the two components will double, one component remaining unshifted and the other increasing in ionisation energy by $\frac{8}{3}$ eV. In figure 58.3 it can be seen that these expectations appear to be borne out, although a small increase instead of none is observed for the orbital of lowest ionisation energy deriving from $1e_{1g}$ of benzene. This discrepancy can be put down to factors not taken into account by this simple theory, which neglects overlap and non-nearest-neighbour interactions. The shifts of the bands deriving from the $1a_{2u}$ member of benzene are accounted for in a similar manner.

In the $3e_{2g}$ orbitals of benzene, as already mentioned, a nodal plane lies along a pair of C—H bonds in one orbital, whereas in the other this pair of bonds is strongly bonded (figure 57.1). The orbital with the nodal plane mentioned is expected to suffer an increase in ionisation energy in pyridine and twice as large an increase in pyrazine (equation (58.1)). The other orbital deriving from the $3e_{2g}$ benzenoid pair is lowered in ionisation energy by the loss of the CH proton. Similar effects are observed in the case of the orbitals deriving from $3e_{1u}$ of benzene.

Problems

1 The spectrum of $C_2(NMe_2)_4$ has peaks at 5·95, 7·5, 7·85, 8·5 and 9·5 eV, whilst that of $B_2(NMe_2)_4$ has peaks at 7·3, 7·6, 9·0 and 9·5 eV (Cetinkaya *et al* 1971). Plot a correlation diagram assuming that the order of ionisation of the orbitals is the same in both compounds. Account for the extra peak in the C compound; would you expect this compound to be a reducing agent?

2 What is the maximum number of bands you would expect to find in the photoelectron spectrum of glutaronitrile, $NC.CH_2.CH_2.CN$, using He(I) 21·21 eV radiation?

3 The coefficients of the molecular orbitals of a cyclic polyene are given in the Hückel approximation by

$$c_{rj} = (2/n)^{1/2} \cos \theta, \qquad (2/n)^{1/2} \sin \theta$$

$$\theta = \frac{2\pi r(j-1)}{n}$$

unless $\theta = 0$ when all the coefficients are $(1/n)^{1/2}$. r is the position in the ring; j is the number of the orbital, with a maximum value of n, and n is the number of atoms in the ring.

Derive the coefficients for the benzene orbitals, verifying figure 58.1. Write the degenerate functions in the form of equation (7.1).

4 In acetonitrile (CH_3CN) the ionisation energy of the pi molecular orbital is 12·18 eV. In methylacetylene, CH_3CCH, the corresponding orbital ionises at 10·37 eV. Account for the shift in energy. The second band in the spectrum of CH_3CN at 13·11 eV is due to the ionisation of an orbital largely consisting of $N(2p)$ character directed along the molecular axis. How do you expect this orbital to change in energy in CH_3CCH?

8 Molecules Related to Xenon Difluoride

59 Xenon Difluoride, XeF₂

The fluorides of xenon, XeF_2, XeF_4 and XeF_6, are colourless, crystalline solids which melt at 140, ~114 and 46 °C, respectively. According to an *ab initio* calculation (Bagus *et al* 1975) the electronic configuration of XeF_2 in order of increasing ionisation energy is $(5\pi_u)^4(10\sigma_g)^2(3\pi_g)^4(4\pi_u)^4(7\sigma_u)^2 \ldots$, and this confirms a simple molecular orbital treatment used by Coulson (1964). Because of the chemical insight which it gives, Coulson's method is described here.

The valence configuration of Xe is $5s^25p^6$, that of F is $2s^22p^5$, and the first important point to be established is that only the p electrons need to be considered in order to explain the spectrum up to about 20 eV, since the s electrons ionise above 23 eV or so. XeF_2 is a linear molecule whose the bond length is 2·01 Å, and at this distance the $\sigma-\sigma$ overlap has about the same magnitude as in F_2. The $\pi-\pi$ interaction is smaller than the $\sigma-\sigma$ and consequently, as we shall see, all the pi orbitals deriving from the valence atomic orbitals are occupied, whilst the uppermost sigma orbital is unoccupied.

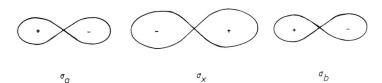

σ_a $\qquad\qquad$ σ_x $\qquad\qquad$ σ_b

Figure 59.1. The arrangement of the atomic orbitals of sigma symmetry XeF_2.

The central atom is labelled x and the F atoms are labelled a and b (figure 59.1). The sigma orbitals of the molecule can be derived on symmetry grounds as

$$7\sigma_u = \sigma_a + \lambda\sigma_x + \sigma_b \tag{59.1}$$

$$10\sigma_g = \sigma_a - \sigma_b \tag{59.2}$$

$$8\sigma_u = \sigma_a - \mu\sigma_x + \sigma_b. \tag{59.3}$$

$7\sigma_u$ is a bonding orbital rather like that labelled $3\sigma_u^+$ for CO_2 in figure 31.2. The $10\sigma_g$ orbital possesses a mirror plane bisecting the molecule perpendicularly to the axis. Since it receives no contribution from the p orbital of the central atom, $10\sigma_g$ is non-bonding as far as p orbitals are concerned (the F(2p) overlap being small), but the inclusion of s character into the central atom causes it to become slightly antibonding.

Equations exactly similar to (59.1)–(59.3) can be written for the pi orbitals. These derive from the p atomic orbitals of the system directed perpendicularly to the molecular axis, thus $3\pi_g$, for example, is

$$\pi_a - \pi_b$$

and the corresponding orbital of CO_2 is $1\pi_g$ of figure 31.2. Because π–π interaction between component p orbitals is smaller in magnitude than σ–σ in this system, the pi orbitals are less separated in energy than are the sigma orbitals (figure 59.2). Of the complete set of orbitals only $8\sigma_u$ is unoccupied in XeF_2.

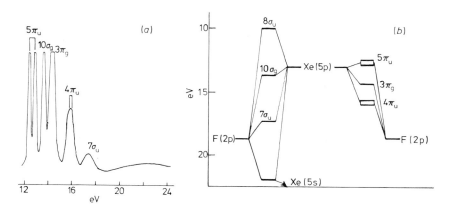

Figure 59.2. (*a*) The photoelectron spectrum of XeF_2 (Brundle *et al* 1971) obtained using He(II) radiation (40·77 eV). The spin–orbit splitting of the $4\pi_u$ band appears in this spectrum only as a slight asymmetry. (*b*) Orbital diagrams of XeF_2 showing ionisation energies. The Xe(5s) level is about 23·4 eV.

The pi orbitals together contribute nothing towards the polarity of the molecule, since they are fully occupied by the electrons. $8\sigma_u$ is empty and $10\sigma_g$ is a purely F(2p) orbital so that it is also non-polar. Consequently, the only orbital which causes charge flow in the molecule is $7\sigma_u$.

The parameter controlling the polarity of the bond is therefore λ (equation (59.1)) and its value can be calculated with the help of some relationships of Pauling (1960). He defines the 'partial ionic character', I, of a bond and relates it to the electronegativities of the atoms, 1 and 2, comprising the bond by

$$I = 1 - \exp\{-0·25(\chi_1 - \chi_2)^2\} \tag{59.4}$$

where χ_1 is the electronegativity of atom 1, etc.

The charge on an atom is given by the sum of the values of I for all the bonds attached to it. For Xe, the electronegativity is 2·25 and for F it is 4·00, hence the charge on each of the F atoms is 0·535 (electronic charges). In order to compare this value with the charge on the F atoms given by equation (59.1), it is first necessary to normalise the equation thus,

$$7\sigma_u = (2 + \lambda^2)^{-1/2}(\sigma_a + \lambda\sigma_x + \sigma_b)$$

where it is assumed that the atomic orbitals are normalised. The charge on an F atom due to a full complement of electrons in this orbital is $2/(2+\lambda^2)$. Of the five electrons of 2p designation on each F atom, four are in the pi orbitals and one is in the $10\sigma_g$ orbital, so that the charge of 0·535 electrons calculated by Pauling's equation must arise by the removal of charge from the central atom, and can be equated with $2/(2+\lambda^2)$. Hence $\lambda = \sqrt{1\cdot74}$.

The orthogonality of equations (59.1) and (59.3) requires that

$$\langle\sigma_a|\sigma_a\rangle - \lambda\mu\langle\sigma_x|\sigma_x\rangle + \langle\sigma_b|\sigma_b\rangle = 0 \tag{59.5}$$

hence

$$\lambda\mu = 2. \tag{59.6}$$

The value of μ is evidently $\sqrt{2\cdot3}$. If the Hückel determinant is solved for XeF_2 with equal values for the Coulomb integrals, that is, with equal electronegativities, then $\lambda = \mu = \sqrt{2}$. Where the value of λ is less than $\sqrt{2}$, charge flows off the central atom, and where it is greater than $\sqrt{2}$, charge flows in the opposite direction.

Table 59.1. Ionisation energies (peak maxima) of XeF_2 and KrF_2 (Brundle *et al* 1970c, Brundle and Jones 1972).

	XeF_2	KrF_2
$5\pi_u$	12·42, 12·89	13·34, 13·47
$10\sigma_g$	13·65	13·90
$3\pi_g$	14·35	14·37
$4\pi_u$	15·60, 16·00	16·92
$7\sigma_u$	17·53	17·7

Ionisation energies are given in table 59.1. The peaks due to the ionisation of orbitals of pi symmetry undergo spin–orbit splitting, but $3\pi_g$, which contains no component from the heavy atom, does not show a detectable effect. The first band in the spectrum of XeF_2 is found to be split by 0·47 eV and the value of μ' (the equivalent of μ in equation (59.3)) can be evaluated from this result. For Xe(5p) the spin–orbit coupling constant is $-0\cdot87$ eV and the fraction of Xe(5p) character in the 3π orbital is therefore $0\cdot47/0\cdot87 = 0\cdot54$. The fraction calculated from the wavefunction is

$$\frac{\mu'^2}{2+\mu'^2} = 0\cdot54$$

hence $\mu' = \sqrt{2\cdot34}$. Since $\mu'\lambda' = 2$ (equation (59.6)) we can obtain the value of λ', and hence the splitting of the $4\pi_u$ band is calculated to be 0·40 eV. This splitting is observed in the fourth band of the spectrum.

In KrF_2 the bands corresponding to $10\sigma_g$ and $3\pi_g$ are expected to occur at the same wavelength as in XeF_2 since they contain no heavy-atom component in the corresponding orbitals. This part of the theory is satisfactorily borne out (table 59.1). Spin–orbit splitting in the first band of KrF_2 is rather less than it would be if the value of μ' were unchanged from its value in XeF_2. No splitting is evident in the other pi bands.

The higher fluorides of Xe are susceptible to the same theoretical treatment. In XeF_4 another set of orbitals of the same type is added at 90° to the first, as the molecule is square planar in shape. However, the spectra of the fluorides of Xe are rather crowded with bands, and overlapping makes assignment rather difficult (Brundle *et al* 1971).

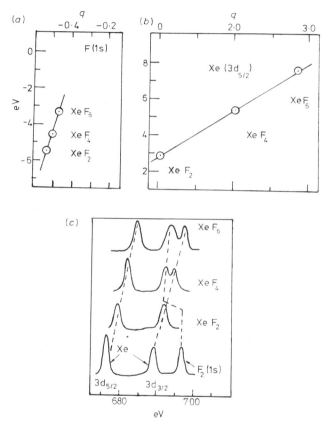

Figure 59.3. (*a*) Charge *q* calculated by equation (59.4), against chemical shift for the F(1s) peak in fluorides of xenon. (*b*) Charge *q* calculated as above against chemical shift of the $Xe(3d_{5/2})$ peak in fluorides of xenon. The point for Xe itself is collinear. (*c*) Photoelectron spectra of the fluorides of Xe showing the peaks attributable to F(1s) and Xe(3d). The spin–orbit separation of the $3d_{5/2}$ and the $3d_{3/2}$ peaks is about 12·7 eV (1486 eV radiation; Carroll *et al* 1974).

There is no problem in the interpretation of that part of the spectrum, obtained with x-radiation, corresponding to the ionisation of Xe(3d) and F(1s) (figure 59.3). Of particular interest here is the correlation of the 'chemical shift' of the peaks with the charge on the atom (Siegbahn *et al* 1969). The chemical shift is defined as the energy difference between the peak in question and the corresponding peak in a reference compound. Thus relative to the position in F_2, the F(1s) peak lies at $-5·48$ eV (XeF_2), $-4·60$ eV (XeF_4), $-3·38$ eV (XeF_6) and $-3·62$ eV ($XeOF_4$) (Carroll *et al* 1974).

The ionisation of a core electron can be approximately treated as the removal of unit negative charge from a sphere. Assuming that the energy to do this is given by Coulomb's law, a linear relationship between the ionisation energy and the charge on the atom is expected. The charge is readily calculated by equation (59.4), but care must be taken to ensure that the electronegativity values employed are corrected for the effect that the charge itself has upon them. We shall assume that the adoption of one unit of charge places the electronegativity about half-way towards that of the next element in the periodic table. Thus, as we have seen, the charge on the central atom in XeF_2 is calculated to be $+1\cdot07$ so that in XeF_4 the second pair of F atoms is attached to an atom with an electronegativity half-way between that of Xe and I. The appropriate value is $\frac{1}{2}(2\cdot4+2\cdot25)$, and the charge on the central atom in XeF_4 is $+2\cdot01$. Taking another half-increment in electronegativity for the increased charge, the electronegativity of Xe^{2+} is equal to that of I itself, and in XeF_6 there is calculated to be a charge of $2\cdot84$ on the central atom.

In spite of the imprecise nature of the argument, the charges calculated above are quite close (and proportional to) the charges on the F atoms calculated by an SCF method. The SCF values are $-0\cdot65$ (XeF_2), $-0\cdot61$ (XeF_4) and $-0\cdot58$ (XeF_6) (Carroll *et al* 1974), compared with values calculated by Pauling's method of $-0\cdot54$, $-0\cdot50$ and $-0\cdot47$. A linear plot of charge against chemical shift is obtained (figure 59.3).

60   Carbon Dioxide and its Derivatives

In XeF_2, as we have seen, the valence s orbitals of the central atom can be neglected for the purpose of obtaining a simple theory for molecular orbitals ionising below 20 eV. In CO_2 this is not the case, since the valence orbital ionisation energy for C(2s) is 19·5 eV (see Appendix III). This 2s atomic orbital of C mixes with the orbital similar to that labelled $10\sigma_g$ in § 59, to form a bonding and an antibonding combination. The bonding resultant is shown in figure 31.2, where it is denoted $4\sigma_g^+$ and it can be seen that it is more bonding than the purely p–p bonding $3\sigma_u^+$ molecular orbital ($7\sigma_u$ in XeF_2).

The linear molecules of the series CO_2, CS_2, CSe_2, $COSe$, etc, have six less valence electrons than XeF_2, and consequently the orbitals corresponding to the $5\pi_u$ members of the XeF_2 set are unoccupied. In addition, the above-mentioned antibonding combination of C(1s) and the orbital correlating with $10\sigma_g$ are unoccupied. The first band in the spectra of the series is therefore attributed to the $1\pi_g$ ionisation. Since this band is due to a non-bonding orbital it is invariably sharp—so sharp that the spin–orbit splitting has been resolved. It will be recalled that this was not possible in the corresponding band of XeF_2. The observed splittings, 0·02 eV (CO_2), 0·05 eV (CS_2) and 0·26 eV (CSe_2) (Cradock and Duncan 1974), are found to be in good agreement with the values of the one-electron spin–orbit coupling constants of the outer atoms (table 36.1). This result is in accordance with the absence of central atom component in $1\pi_g$.

Equation (58.1) can be used to relate the spectra of the series. The value of $-\Delta(H_{aa})$ relevant to a substitution of, for example, an O atom for an S atom can be equated to the difference in valence orbital ionisation energies, that is, $11\cdot7-15\cdot9=4\cdot2$ eV. For the $1\pi_g$ orbital, $c^2=\frac{1}{2}$, and starting with an ionisation energy of

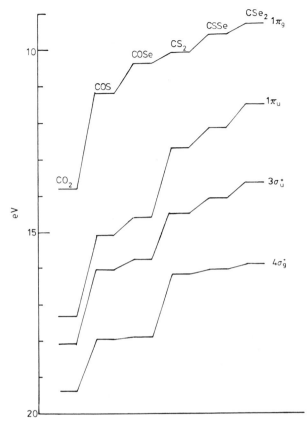

Figure 60.1. Correlation of the ionisation energies of molecules related to CO_2 (Frost *et al* 1973a).

13·8 eV for CO_2, it is possible to calculate the energy of this band in the other molecules within about 0·7 eV by the above method. Thus in SCSe the ionisation energy of the first band is estimated to be $13·8 - \frac{1}{2}(4·2 + 5·1) = 9·15$ eV, as compared with the observed energy of 9·58 eV (Frost *et al* 1973a; figure 60.1). In the same way, the energies of the other bands can be calculated. It is noteworthy that a fairly large change in energy is predicted on going from CO_2 to CS_2, but a smaller one on proceeding to CSe_2, as has been observed.

61   Nitrous oxide, N_2O, and its Derivatives

Nitrous oxide, N—N—O, is a linear molecule which is isoelectronic with carbon dioxide. The sequence of ionisation energies is given in figure 61.1 for nitrous oxide, fulminic acid (H—N—C—O), diazomethane (H_2C—N—N) and hydrazoic acid (HN—N—N), all isoelectronic molecules.

An interesting question is the relative stability of the isomers N—O—N and N—N—O. According to Pauling (1970) the isomerisation energy can be approxi-

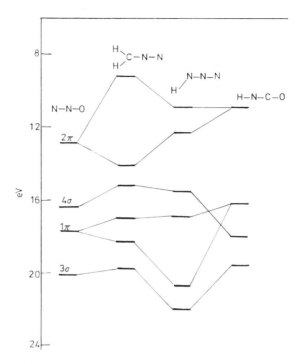

Figure 61.1. Molecules isoelectronic with nitrous oxide; correlation of the bands observed in the photoelectron spectra (Bastide and Maier 1976). Note the raising of the degeneracy of the pi orbitals upon the loss of linearity.

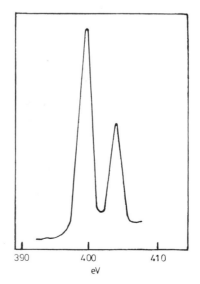

Figure 61.2. Photoelectron spectrum of sodium azide (solid) in the N(1s) region (Siegbahn *et al* 1967).

mately calculated as the difference in nuclear repulsion energies, since the electronic structures in the two isomers are closely similar. Repulsion energies are calculated for the 'kernels' of the atoms, which can be defined as the nuclei plus the 1s electrons. For O, the charge on the kernel is +6 and for N it is +5. The N–N separation distance is $1\cdot13$ Å and the N–O separation distance is $1\cdot19$ Å; hence if the Coulombic repulsion energy for a pair of electronic charges separated by 1 Å is $14\cdot4$ eV, the energy for the N–O–N kernels is $14\cdot4\times2\times5\times6/1\cdot19=726$ eV. The isomerisation energy is the difference between the repulsive energies of the two isomers multiplied by an empirical constant. For this constant, Pauling (1970) gives a value of $0\cdot1$, and hence the isomerisation energy is found to be $4\cdot45$ eV.

In the Franck–Condon state following the loss of a 1s electron from a nitrogen atom, the kernel possesses one positive unit of charge more than it did before the photoeffect took place; it therefore appears to be an oxygen kernel. As far as the valence electrons are concerned, therefore, the ionisation

$$N(1s^2\ldots)+h\nu=N^+(1s^1\ldots)+e^-$$

is equivalent to

$$N(1s^2\ldots)+h\nu=O(1s^2\ldots).$$

In sodium azide the linear N_3^- ion has an N–N distance of $1\cdot15$ Å. There are two peaks in the region of the spectrum where N(1s) is expected to ionise (figure 61.2). One of these peaks has twice the intensity of the other; this is attributed to the ionisation of the two non-central atoms, and the other is attributed to the ionisation of the central atom. The energy separation of the peaks is caused by the differing charges on the two types of atom; the central one bears a charge of about $0\cdot64$ and the outer pair have charges of about $-0\cdot72$ electronic units. From the point of view of the valence electrons, the ionisation processes responsible for the two peaks can be written

$$(N-N-N)^-+h\nu=(N-O-N)^-$$

$$(N-N-N)^-+h\nu=(O-N-N)^-$$

and the difference in energy between the two can be equated with the isomerisation energy (Jolly 1972). The ionisation energies are $399\cdot2$ and $403\cdot7$ eV (Siegbahn *et al* 1967); hence the isomerisation energy is $4\cdot5$ eV, which is in agreement with the value calculated from the kernel repulsions, although the remarkable precision is certainly fortuitous.

62 Fluorine and Chlorine Monoxides

Fluorine monoxide, F_2O, is a colourless gas in which the F–O distance is $1\cdot358$ Å and the F–O–F angle is $103\cdot8°$. Since the electronegativity of oxygen is higher than that of xenon, it is expected that the polarity is less than that of XeF_2, but the chief difference between the compounds arises from the nonlinearity of F_2O. The point group is C_{2v} and the pi orbitals of figure 59.2 lose their degeneracy, as shown in figure 62.1. There are two electrons less in F_2O than in XeF_2, and the first band in

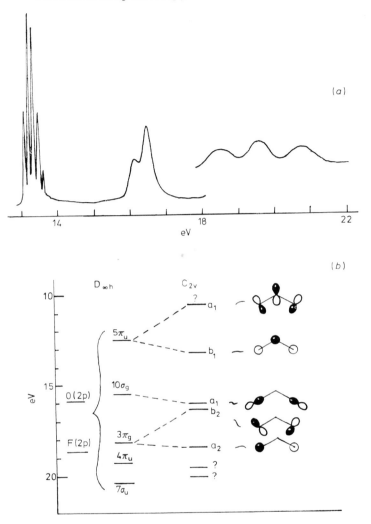

Figure 62.1. (*a*) The photoelectron spectrum of F_2O (Brundle *et al* 1972b). Below 18 eV the light was of energy 21·21 eV and above 18 eV it was of energy 40·77 eV. The progression of totally symmetric stretching vibrations in the first band has a separation interval of 1032 cm^{-1}, as compared with 929 cm^{-1} in the neutral molecule. (*b*) Molecular orbital energy diagram correlating the observed ionisation energies of F_2O with those of XeF_2.

the photoelectron spectrum is the b_1 component of the orbitals corresponding to $5\pi_u$ in XeF_2. That this first band is indeed derived from the ionisation of an antibonding orbital is clear from the analysis of the well developed vibrational structure (Cornford *et al* 1971), where a progression of O—F stretching vibrations is observed with the frequency increased from its value in the neutral molecule.

The pair of bands lying between 16 and 17 eV are assigned to the non-bonding and antibonding a_1 and b_2 molecular orbitals, respectively, and the third band (at about 18·5 eV) is assigned to the lower a_2 component derived from $3\pi_g$ of XeF_2.

At higher energies there appears to be some overlapping of the peaks and positive conclusions are not possible. Calculations of the ionisation energies have been carried out by subtraction of the scf energies of the ionic states from those of the neutral molecule (Brundle *et al* 1972b). Calculated values are 13·5 eV (b_+), 16·3 eV (a_1), 16·9 eV (b_2) and 18·3 eV (a_2). Peak maxima were observed at 13·25, 16·1, 16·44 and 18·50 eV, respectively.

Chlorine monoxide, Cl_2O, is a brown gas with a Cl–O distance of 1·701 Å and a Cl–O–Cl angle of 110·8°. Chlorine is less electronegative than fluorine, so that the Cl–O bond is less polar than the F–O bond. Using equation (58.1) it can be established that the ionisation energies of Cl_2O should be a few electron volts less than those of F_2O, and this is found to be the case. In Cl_2O the first b_1 ionisation lies at 11·02 eV, as compared with 13·25 eV in F_2O. Subsequent bands are at 12·4 eV (a_1), 12·7 eV (b_2) and 12·8 eV (a_2) (Cornford *et al* 1971).

Problems

1 Using equation (59.4) calculate the ionicity of HF (see § 20). $\chi_H = 2\cdot1$, $\chi_F = 4\cdot0$.

2 The cyanogen halides (XCN) are linear molecules which are isoelectronic with CO_2. Account for the fact that the first band in the spectrum is split; ClCN, 12·34 and 12·37 eV; BrCN, 11·88 and 12·07 eV; ICN, 10·91 and 11·45 eV. Using the method of § 60 explain why these ionisation energies increase with the atomic number of the halogen.

3 Give an explanation of the changes in ionisation energy of the band labelled 4σ in figure 61.1.

9 Tetrahedral Molecules

63 Tetrahedrally Disposed p Orbitals

The point group of the tetrahedron is T_d (table 41.1) and some of the operations are depicted in figure 63.1. The first two sections of this chapter are given to the solution of a frequent problem—the elucidation of the molecular orbitals formed by a tetrahedral array of p orbitals.

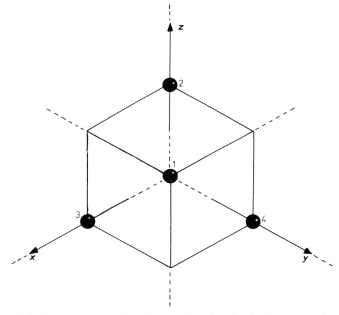

Figure 63.1. Symmetry operations of a tetrahedral molecule. Atoms are shown as solid spheres, and are at the alternate corners of the cube. The x, y and z axes pass through the centres of the faces shown, the origin of the coordinates being at the centre of the cube. The axes are also twofold rotation axes. Broken lines indicate mirror planes perpendicular to the plane of the paper. That x, y and z are also S_4 axes can be seen by imagining there to be a fourfold rotation about one of them, say x, followed by reflection in the yz plane.

There is freedom of choice as to how the p orbitals are directed in space, but it is possible to choose an orientation such that the resulting integrals are easily evaluated. It is convenient to divide the p orbitals into two classes according to their geometrical relationship with the centre; σ orbitals pointing towards the centre and

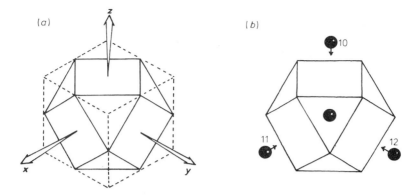

Figure 63.2. (*a*) The derivation of the cuboctahedron from the cube, looking down the C_3 axis. (*b*) The σ orbitals, showing their numbering and orientation. These orbitals point towards the centre of the figure.

π orbitals pointing perpendicularly to the centre (figure 63.2). This classification with respect to the central atom means that the descriptions σ and π do not have their usual meaning when we discuss the interactions of the p orbitals among one another, but so long as this is remembered there should be no confusion.

It is difficult to show clearly the orientation of the pi orbitals in two-dimensional drawings, but it is a simple matter to construct from thin cardboard a three-

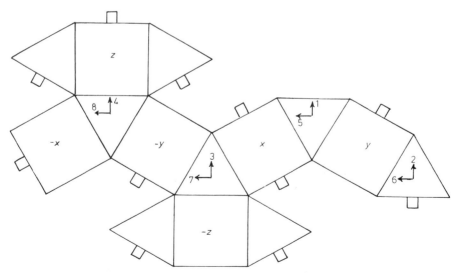

Figure 63.3. The geometry of the tetrahedral array of p orbitals is best displayed by means of a three-dimensional figure. The cuboctahedron can be made by ruling the lines (with all edges equal) on cardboard, lightly scoring with a knife, and sticking the faces together with the flaps. A convenient edge length is between 4 and 7 cm. The directions of the p orbitals of pi symmetry are shown by arrows, numbered 1–8. Note that this is the outside surface.

dimensional model. Instructions for doing this are given in figure 63.3. The model is based on the cuboctahedron which is derived from the cube by cutting off the vertices so that equilateral triangles appear in their places. The π orbitals, numbered 1–8, then lie on alternate triangles. The flat figure of 63.3 is itself a useful map of the tetrahedral system.

64 Molecular Orbitals Formed by Tetrahedrally Disposed p Orbitals

In order to discover what irreducible representations are spanned by the basis consisting of the p orbitals of § 63, it is necessary to find out how the orbitals transform under the operations of the T_d point group. This process has been described in previous sections, such as § 22.

Having proceeded so far, a rigorous way of putting together the p orbitals so as to obtain a molecular orbital transforming with the correct symmetry is to apply every operation of the group (24 in all) to one set of orbitals, say 1, 5 and 9. The result for every operation is then multiplied by the character of the operation in the irreducible representation required, and the sum of these resultants is the desired molecular orbital (although not always in the desired form).

Table 64.1. Transformation table for ligand orbitals under the operations of tetrahedral symmetry. The C_3 axis corresponds to the vertical axis of figure 63.2(a).

E	C_3	$C_2(z)$	$S_4(z)$	σ_d
1	$1(-\tfrac{1}{2})+5(-\sqrt{3}/2)$	4	−3	4
2	$3(-\tfrac{1}{2})+7(-\sqrt{3}/2)$	3	−1	2
3	$4(\tfrac{1}{2})+8(\sqrt{3}/2)$	2	−4	3
4	$2(\tfrac{1}{2})+6(\sqrt{3}/2)$	1	−2	1
5	$5(-\tfrac{1}{2})+1(\sqrt{3}/2$	8	7	−8
6	$7(-\tfrac{1}{2})+3(\sqrt{3}/2)$	7	5	−6
7	$8(\tfrac{1}{2})+4(-\sqrt{3}/2)$	6	8	−7
8	$6(\tfrac{1}{2})+2(-\sqrt{3}/2)$	5	6	−5
9	9	12	11	12
10	11	11	9	10
11	12	10	12	11
12	10	9	10	9

Table 64.1 gives the results of a few of the 24 operations, and can be verified by inspection of the model described in figure 63.3. The table will be used here to form the molecular orbitals by a simplified procedure which requires less operations than the above method, and is therefore less liable to error.

Inspection of the three-dimensional model confirms that an orbital of t_2 symmetry transforming like z is composed of π orbitals, $1+2+3+4$, and σ orbitals, $-9-12+10+11$. A negative sign implies a change in direction by 180°. Assuming that the atomic orbitals are normalised, the molecular orbitals in their normalised forms are

$$t_2(z, \pi) = \tfrac{1}{2}(\underline{1} + \underline{2} + \underline{3} + \underline{4}) \tag{64.1}$$

$$t_2(z, \sigma) = \tfrac{1}{2}(-\underline{9} - \underline{12} + \underline{10} + \underline{11}). \tag{64.2}$$

A threefold rotation around the axis chosen in table 64.1 takes z into y and hence the $t_2(y)$ orbitals corresponding to the above are obtained with the C_3 operator.

Table 64.2. Molecular orbitals of a set of tetrahedrally disposed p orbitals.

		Derived from π orbitals
1	$e(z^2)$	$\tfrac{1}{2}(-\underline{1} + \underline{2} + \underline{3} - \underline{4})$
2	$e(x^2 - y^2)$	$\tfrac{1}{2}(\underline{5} - \underline{6} - \underline{7} + \underline{8})$
3	$t_2(z)$	$\tfrac{1}{2}(\underline{1} + \underline{2} + \underline{3} + \underline{4})$
4	$t_2(y)$	$\tfrac{1}{4}(-\underline{1} + \underline{2} - \underline{3} + \underline{4}) + \sqrt{3}/4(-\underline{5} + \underline{6} - \underline{7} + \underline{8})$
5	$t_2(x)$	$\tfrac{1}{4}(-\underline{1} - \underline{2} + \underline{3} + \underline{4}) + \sqrt{3}/4(\underline{5} + \underline{6} - \underline{7} - \underline{8})$
6	$t_1(R_z)$	$\tfrac{1}{2}(\underline{5} + \underline{6} + \underline{7} + \underline{8})$
7	$t_1(R_y)$	$\tfrac{1}{4}(-\underline{5} + \underline{6} - \underline{7} + \underline{8}) + \sqrt{3}/4(\underline{1} - \underline{2} + \underline{3} - \underline{4})$
8	$t_1(R_x)$	$\tfrac{1}{4}(-\underline{5} - \underline{6} + \underline{7} + \underline{8}) + \sqrt{3}/4(-\underline{1} - \underline{2} + \underline{3} + \underline{4})$
		Derived from σ orbitals
9	a_1	$\tfrac{1}{2}(\underline{9} + \underline{10} + \underline{11} + \underline{12})$
10	$t_2(z)$	$\tfrac{1}{2}(-\underline{9} + \underline{10} + \underline{11} - \underline{12})$
11	$t_2(x)$	$\tfrac{1}{2}(-\underline{9} + \underline{10} - \underline{11} + \underline{12})$
12	$t_2(y)$	$\tfrac{1}{2}(-\underline{9} - \underline{10} + \underline{11} + \underline{12})$

Using the results in table 64.1 we derive

$$t_2(y, \sigma) = \tfrac{1}{2}(-\underline{9} - \underline{10} + \underline{11} + \underline{12})$$

and another C_3 operation gives

$$t_2(x, \sigma) = \tfrac{1}{2}(-\underline{9} + \underline{10} - \underline{11} + \underline{12}).$$

In the same way, the t_1 orbitals can be generated by repeated C_3 operations on the orbital transforming as R_z, namely, $\tfrac{1}{2}(\underline{5} + \underline{6} + \underline{7} + \underline{8})$. In table 64.2 the complete set of results is given.

65 Energies of Tetrahedral Orbitals

In this section Hückel energies are computed for the orbitals of § 64. The chief requirement here is the simplification of the results: for example, the energy of the $e(z^2)$ orbital of table 64.2 is

$$\langle \psi | H | \psi \rangle = \tfrac{1}{4}(H_{11} + H_{22} + H_{33} + H_{44}) + \tfrac{1}{2}(-H_{12} - H_{13} + H_{14} + H_{23} - H_{24} - H_{34}).$$

Many of the terms in the above equation have the same value. All the Coulomb integrals, H_{ii}, are equal and will be denoted by α. The values of the resonance terms H_{ij} depend on the geometrical relationship of the ith and the jth orbitals with respect to each other. In determining these relationships, figure 63.3 is invaluable:

for example, it is evident that

$$H_{12} = H_{13} = H_{24} = H_{34}$$

and the energy of $e(z^2)$ can now be written

$$H_{11} - 2H_{12} + H_{14}.$$

As mentioned earlier, figure 63.3 in its flat form is a map of the tetrahedral molecule. In abbreviated form it can be written

$$2 \quad 4 \quad 3 \quad 1 \quad 2$$
$$+ \quad - \quad + \quad - \quad .$$
$$7 \quad 5 \quad 6 \quad 8 \quad 7$$

Pairs in the same relationship in the above have the same integral. Thus $H_{24} = H_{31} = H_{12}$ and $H_{23} = H_{41}$. The plus and minus signs indicate that $H_{25} = -H_{46} = -H_{35}$, etc. Vertically related pairs have zero integrals; $H_{27} = 0$. Pairs related by a 'knight's move'† also have zero integrals; $H_{26} = H_{15} = 0$. Note that $H_{75} \neq H_{24}$, that is, the top row is not equivalent to the bottom row.

In addition to the Coulomb integral, α, it is convenient to define two more integrals, π and σ, these being the resonance integrals H_{ij}, where $i \neq j$. In the pi interaction the p orbitals are directed perpendicularly to the line joining i and j (they are not in pi orientation with respect to the centre). For example,

$$-H_{58} = \pi.$$

That this is so can be verified with the aid of the solid model, but no pair of orbitals can be found pointing at each other in exactly σ fashion. It is possible, using the three-dimensional model, to resolve every integral into its components: for example,

$$H_{14} = \pi(\cos 30)^2 + \sigma(\cos 60)^2$$
$$= \tfrac{3}{4}\pi + \tfrac{1}{4}\sigma.$$

Again the σ integral refers to an orientation in which the involved p orbitals point directly at each other and not at the central atom.

Table 65.1. H_{ij} integrals between tetra-hedrally disposed p orbitals resolved into Coulomb (α) and resonance integrals (π and σ).

H_{11}	α
H_{67}	$-\pi$
H_{23}	$\tfrac{3}{4}\pi + \tfrac{1}{4}\sigma$
$H_{9,10}$	$\tfrac{3}{4}\sigma + \tfrac{1}{4}\pi$
H_{56}	$-(5/16)\pi - (3/16)\sigma$
H_{52}	$-(7\sqrt{3}/16)\pi - (\sqrt{3}/16)\sigma$
H_{12}	$(9/16)\pi - (1/16)\sigma$

† This term is borrowed from the game of chess. It means a jump from one row to the other followed by two moves along a row.

Table 65.2. Energies of molecular orbitals of tetrahedrally disposed p orbitals.

Derived from π orbitals	
Symmetry	Eigenvalue
e	$\alpha - (3/8)\pi + (3/8)\sigma$
t_2	$\alpha + (15/8)\pi + (1/8)\sigma$
t_1	$\alpha - (13/8)\pi - (3/8)\sigma$
Derived from σ orbitals	
a_1	$\alpha + \tfrac{3}{4}\pi + (9/4)\sigma$
t_2	$\alpha - \tfrac{1}{4}\pi - \tfrac{3}{4}\sigma$

In table 65.1 the complete set of relationships is given. The energy of the molecular orbital of $e(z^2)$ symmetry can now be written

$$H_{11} - 2H_{12} + H_{14} = \alpha - (3/8)\pi + (3/8)\sigma.$$

The remaining energies are given in table 65.2.

66 Tetraphosphorus, P₄

The results of the preceeding sections are now applied to the colourless, metastable allotrope of phosphorus, P_4. The geometry is tetrahedral, the P–P distance is 2·21 Å and the valence configuration of P is $3s^2 3p^3$. In the vapour state at room temperature, P_4 is the stable form but it dissociates to $2P_2$ at high temperatures.

The photoelectron spectrum is shown in figure 66.1. The bands in the spectrum around 10 eV are expected to consist mainly of 3p orbitals, the valence orbital ionisation energy being 10·2 eV (see Appendix III). The broad band at between 15 and 18 eV, which shows evidence of Jahn–Teller splitting into three components, is largely derived from 3s orbitals (VOIE = 18·7 eV).

The relative energies of the p-derived orbitals can be calculated from the results in table 65.2 if the ratio of the magnitudes of the π and the σ orbitals is known. According to Mulliken (1949) a good approximation for this ratio is the ratio of the corresponding overlap integrals, $S(\sigma)/S(\pi)$. The overlap integrals are readily calculated using Slater orbitals, and the ratio for P(3p) at 2·21 Å comes out at 2·26 (Mulliken *et al* 1949). In order of increasing ionisation energy, the orbitals of table 65.2 therefore have the following energies:

$$t_1(\pi) = -10\cdot2 - 2\cdot47\,\pi$$

$$t_2(\sigma) = -10\cdot2 - 1\cdot95\,\pi$$

$$e(\pi) = -10\cdot2 + 0\cdot47\,\pi$$

$$t_2(\pi) = -10\cdot2 + 2\cdot16\,\pi$$

$$a_1(\sigma) = -10\cdot2 + 5\cdot84\,\pi.$$

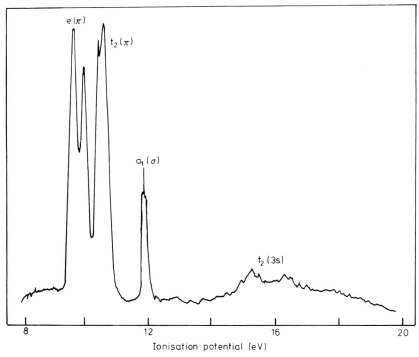

Figure 66.1. The photoelectron spectrum of the tetraphosphorus molecule, P_4, obtained using He(I) radiation (Brundle *et al* 1972a).

The twelve 3p electrons of P_4 occupy $e(\pi)$, $t_2(\pi)$ and $a_1(\sigma)$. These are all bonding; no bonding orbitals are left empty, and the reason for the stability of the molecule is therefore evident. In the frozen approximation the order of ionisation is also that given above, that is, $e(\pi) < t_2(\pi) < a_1(\sigma)$. The first two peaks in the spectrum are therefore expected to be degenerate and both show evidence of splitting by the Jahn–Teller effect, $e(\pi)$ being split the most.

Table 66.1. Observed and calculated energies for P_4 (in eV).

	SCF eigenvalue (Brundle *et al* 1972a	Ionisation energy (equations of table 65.2)†	Ionisation energy (observed)
$t_1(\pi)$	1·78	−9·1	—
$t_2(\sigma)$	1·67	−9·4	—
$e(\pi)$	−10·46	10·4	9·5, 9·9
$t_2(\pi)$	−11·15	11·2	10·4, 10·6
$a_1(\sigma)$	−12·45	12·8	11·87
$t_2(3s)$	−21·00	< 18·7	15·2, 16·3, 17·5
$a_1(3s)$	−31·50	> 18·7	—

† The ionisation energies calculated by the equations of table 65.2 were obtained with the values $\alpha = -10 \cdot 2$ eV and $\pi = -0 \cdot 44$ eV (see text).

The energy difference between the $e(\pi)$ and the $a_1(\sigma)$ peaks is $5 \cdot 37\pi$, the observed difference in ionisation energy is $2 \cdot 37$ eV and hence the approximate value of π is $-0 \cdot 44$ eV. In table $66 \cdot 1$ the ionisation energies calculated with this value are given together with the results of an SCF calculation.

The s orbitals span $t_2 + a_1$, the former being antibonding, and the latter bonding. t_2 would be expected to ionise $1 - 2$ eV below the VOIE of $18 \cdot 7$ eV, but the SCF calculation seems to be in error here. The a_1 orbital is outside the range of He(I) radiation. The molecular orbitals of P(3s) parentage have similar wavefunctions to those derived from P(p, σ) orbitals, that is, numbers 9 to 12 (table 64.2).

The photoelectron spectrum of P_2 has been reported (Bulgin *et al* 1977), the ionisation energies being $10 \cdot 62$ eV ($2\pi_u$), $10 \cdot 81$ eV ($5\sigma_g$) and $15 \cdot 52$ eV ($4\sigma_u$). In this case, unlike N_2, Koopmans' theorem predicts the correct ordering of the ionisation energies. The bond length of P_2 is $0 \cdot 32$ Å shorter than that of P_4.

67 Tetraboron Tetrachloride, B_4Cl_4

Tetraboron tetrachloride is a pale yellow solid which is readily decomposed by moisture. X-ray analysis of the crystal shows it to be a tetrahedron of boron atoms

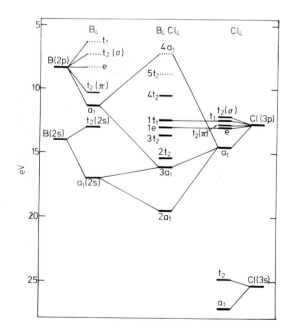

Figure 67.1. Molecular orbitals of B_4Cl_4. Occupied orbitals are indicated by bold lines, and unoccupied orbitals by dotted lines. Approximate energies of the B_4 tetrahedron are given under the heading B_4. Similarly, the approximate energies of Cl_4 are given under the heading Cl_4. The method of calculation is described in the text. Connections between orbitals of a_1 symmetry show how they are related but, for the sake of simplicity, corresponding connections for the t_2 orbitals have been omitted. For B_4Cl_4 the observed energies are plotted (Lloyd and Lynaugh 1971).

within a tetrahedron of chlorine atoms, the B—Cl links being directed at the centre.

The configurations $B(2s^2 2p^1)$ and $Cl(3s^2 3p^5)$ give 40 valence electrons in B_4Cl_4, which is twice the number found in P_4. We could choose to analyse the bonding in a variety of ways: for example, the diatomic molecule, BCl, could be regarded as the building unit. Instead we shall consider first the tetrahedra B_4 and Cl_4, and then see how they interact in B_4Cl_4.

In figure 67.1 is given an approximate molecular orbital energy diagram showing how the energy levels of B_4 and Cl_4 arise from the valence orbital ionisation energies of the constituent atoms. Then, in the centre of the diagram, the observed ionisation energies of B_4Cl_4 are correlated with the tetrahedral energies.

In making the calculations for Cl_4, the method of § 66 was used with the value $\pi = 0$, on account of the large separation distance between the atoms (4·5 Å). For B_4, the values assumed were, $\pi = \sigma = -1$ eV. For the orbitals derived from $B(2s)$ the energies were

$$E(a_1) = \text{VOIE} + 3\gamma$$

$$E(t_2) = \text{VOIE} - \gamma$$

where γ is the resonance integral $\langle \phi(2s_1)|H|\phi(2s_2)\rangle$. A value of -1 eV was assigned to γ. The reader will conclude that these calculations are hardly likely to be accurate in view of the seeming arbitrariness of the choice of parameter values, but

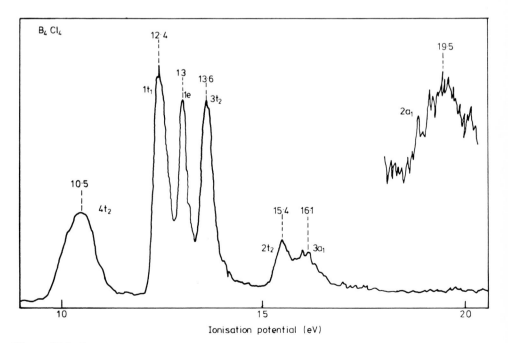

Figure 67.2. The photoelectron spectrum of tetraboron tetrachloride, with tentative assignments, obtained using He(I) resonance radiation (Lloyd and Lynaugh 1971).

figure 67.1 nevertheless demonstrates clearly the nature of the orbitals of B_4Cl_4 and might not be significantly changed by a much more careful estimate.

In the photoelectron spectrum of B_4Cl_4, as in that of P_4, there are peaks standing out because of their intensities. These can be assigned to orbitals which have a large component of $Cl(3p)$ character and are of a non-bonding nature, namely, $3t_2$, $1e$ and $1t_1$. There is little to choose in energy between them, and the order in which they appear in the spectrum is uncertain. The assignments of figure 67.2 are therefore tentative in this region of the spectrum.

68 Group IV Tetrahalides

In the tetrahalides of C, Si, Ge, Sn and Pb, the s^2p^2 valence configuration of the central atom interacts with the orbitals of the tetrahedral array of halogen atoms. The unoccupied d orbitals of the central atom, spanning e and t_2, lie about 10 eV above the valence level and will be neglected.

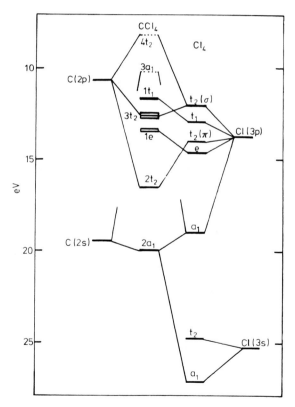

Figure 68.1. Molecular orbitals of CCl_4 (cf figure 67.1). Occupied orbitals are shown by bold lines, and unoccupied orbitals by broken lines. Approximate energies for the tetrahedron are given under the heading Cl_4, calculated by the method described in the text. Observed ionisation energies are given under the heading CCl_4.

Table 68.1. Observed ionisation energies (in eV) for halides and hybrides of group IV.

Compound	$2a_1$	$2t_2$	$1e$	$3t_2$	$1t_1$	Reference
CF_4	25·1	21·95	18·5	17·47	16·23	Potts *et al* (1970)
SiF_4	21·6	19·52	18·09	17·55	16·46	Bull *et al* (1970)
GeF_4	21·3	18·55	17·0	16·5	16·1	Cradock (1971)
CCl_4	20·0	16·58	{13·5, 13·37}	{12·78, 12·65, 12·44}	11·69	Potts *et al* (1970)
$SiCl_4$	17·98	15·13	{13·35, 13·44}	12·85	12·03	Green *et al* (1970)
$GeCl_4$	18·0	{14·7, 14·8, 14·9}	13·08	12·60	12·12	Green *et al* (1970)
$SnCl_4$	17·0	14·0	12·71	{12·50, 12·38}	12·10	Green *et al* (1970)
CBr_4	19·7	15·15	{12·24, 12·11}	{11·73, 11·28, 11·07}	{10·76, 10·48, 10·39}	Potts *et al* (1970)
$SiBr_4$	17·31	{13·92, 14·19}	12·05	{12·05, 11·52}	{11·17, 10·90}	Green *et al* (1970)
$GeBr_4$	17·6	{13·63, 13·70}	11·89	{11·89, 11·23}	{11·11, 10·85}	Green *et al* (1970)
$SnBr_4$	16·7	13·2	11·75	{11·75, 11·25}	{11·25, 11·0}	Green *et al* (1970)
CH_4	22·91	14·35				Potts and Price (1972)
SiH_4	18·17	12·82				Potts and Price (1972)
GeH_4	18·40	12·46				Potts and Price (1972)
SnH_4	16·88	11·27				Potts and Price (1972)

In many respects the molecular energy diagram of CCl_4 (figure 68.1) is similar to that of B_4Cl_4 (figure 67.2). Spectra are given in figure 41.2, and in figure 68.2 a regular pattern can be discerned.

The assignment of the $2a_1$ and the $2t_2$ orbitals seems unequivocal (figure 41.2). The remaining assignments are made partly on account of relative intensity ($1e$ being the weakest since it contains fewest electrons), and partly on account of an

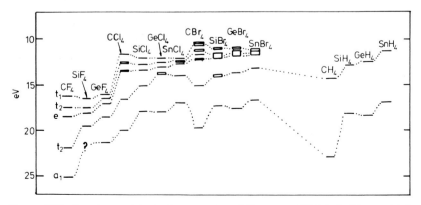

Figure 68.2. the observed ionisation energies of the group IV tetrahalides and tetra-hydrides.

SCF calculation (Brundle *et al* 1970b), although $3t_2$ and $1t_2$ are reversed in other calculations (Lazzeretti and Zanasi 1976, Jonas *et al* 1972).

Both $1t_1$ and $1e$ are non-bonding for the central atom–halogen bond; such as for C—F. As far as the inter-halogen bonds are concerned, $1t_1$ is antibonding and $1e$ is bonding.

In CCl_4 the Cl–Cl separation distance is $3 \cdot 06$ Å, which is large enough for the π integral to be equated to zero. The energy separation of $1e$ and $1t_1$ is therefore $\frac{3}{4}\sigma$ (table 65.2) and the value $\sigma = -2 \cdot 3$ eV follows from the data in table 68.1. With this value and using the valence orbital ionisation energy of $13 \cdot 8$ eV for Cl(3p), the ionisation energies of the Cl_4 tetrahedron in figure 68.1 have been calculated. In fact these calculated energies appear to be too high, probably because polarisation in the sense $C^+–Cl^-$ lowers the ionisation energy of Cl(3p).

The largest bonding interaction in the carbon tetrahalides is that between C(2p) and the t_2 orbitals of the halogens. For example, the overlap populations for C—F calculated by an SCF method (Brundle *et al* 1970b) are $0 \cdot 000$ ($1t_1$), $0 \cdot 026$ ($3t_2$), $0 \cdot 000$ ($1e$), $0 \cdot 064$ ($2t_2$) and $0 \cdot 046$ ($2a_1$).

All the orbitals of the tetrahedron delineated in § 64 are occupied. There are 20 electrons from the halogen and only four from the central atom in these orbitals, and therefore it should come as no surprise to find that the average energies of the ionisations in figure 68.2 are close to the VOIEs of the halogenic p orbitals (see Problem 2, p 162). The observed average energies are $18 \cdot 2$ eV (fluorides), $13 \cdot 6$ eV (chlorides) and $12 \cdot 6$ eV (bromides).

In the tetrahydrides only the $2t_2$ and $2a_1$ orbitals are occupied (figure 68.2) but the ionisation energies follow the same pattern as in the carbon tetrahalides.

69 Group IV Tetramethyls

The elucidation of the spectra of the tetramethyls of group IV follows naturally from the discussion of § 68. Instead of the halogen atoms, there are isoelectronic methyl groups whose molecular orbitals (figure 69.1) replace the atomic orbitals previously discussed. Thus the $2a_1$, $1e$ and $1a_1$ orbitals of the methyl group are substituted for σ–p, π–p and s. The methyl group belongs to the C_{3v} point group and computer calculations give the eigenvalues -29 eV ($1a_1$), $-13 \cdot 9$ eV ($1e$) and $-11 \cdot 7$ eV ($2a_1$) (Jorgensen and Salem 1973).

These eigenvalues replace valence orbital ionisation energies in figure 69.1 where approximate energies of the $(CH_3)_4$ orbitals are given which have been

Table 69.1. Ionisation energies (in eV) of group IV tetramethyls (Evans *et al* 197b).

	$C(CH_3)_4$	$Si(CH_3)_4$	$Ge(CH_3)_4$	$Sn(CH_3)_4$	$Pb(CH_3)_4$
$3t_2$	$\begin{cases}10 \cdot 96 \\ 11 \cdot 44\end{cases}$	$10 \cdot 57$	$10 \cdot 23$	$9 \cdot 79$	$\begin{cases}8 \cdot 81 \\ 9 \cdot 09 \\ 9 \cdot 86\end{cases}$
$1t_1$	$12 \cdot 58$	$13 \cdot 06$	$\sim 13 \cdot 0$	$\sim 13 \cdot 4$	$\sim 13 \cdot 3$
$1e$	$13 \cdot 91$	$14 \cdot 08$	$13 \cdot 85$	$\sim 13 \cdot 4$	$\sim 13 \cdot 3$
$2t_2$	$15 \cdot 24$	$14 \cdot 08$	$13 \cdot 85$	$\sim 13 \cdot 4$	$\sim 13 \cdot 3$
$2a_1$	$17 \cdot 77$	$15 \cdot 58$	$15 \cdot 9$	—	$\sim 15 \cdot 3$

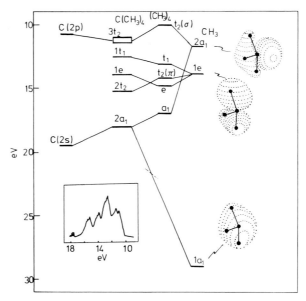

Figure 69.1. Energy diagram for the molecular orbitals of carbon tetramethyl. On the right, electron density contours for the orbitals of the methyl radical are given (Jorgensen and Salem 1973). Under the heading $(CH_3)_4$ are the energies calculated by the method described in the text. The observed ionisation energies are given under the heading $C(CH_3)_4$, and the spectrum is inset (Evans *et al* 1972b).

calculated with the same resonance integrals as for CCl_4 in § 68. The assignments of figure 69.1 agree with a CNDO calculation (Jonas *et al* 1972).

70   Transition Metal Chlorides

Titanium tetrachloride is a colourless liquid which boils at 137 °C and fumes in moist air to give TiO_2 and HCl. The tetrabromide melts at 39 °C, boils at 230 °C, and otherwise has similar properties to $TiCl_4$. Vanadium tetrachloride can be described as a dark red, oily liquid which boils at 154 °C. The spectra of these compounds are plotted in figure 70.1.

TiCl$_4$ and CCl$_4$ are isoelectronic, the valence configuration of Ti being $3d^2 4s^2$. *Ab initio* calculations (Hillier and Kendrick 1976) result in the same order of ionisation energies for $TiCl_4$ as for CCl_4 (figure 68.1). According to this calculation the upper orbitals are mostly $Cl(2p)$ in character, as in CCl_4, although the orbital that we have called $t_2(\pi)$ contains 21% of $V(3d)$ and e contains 16% of this metallic orbital. The Cl–Cl distance is 3·78 Å in $TiCl_4$, 24% greater than in CCl_4, and the interactions in the Cl_4 tetrahedron are greatly reduced.

Since the valence configuration of V is $3d^3 4s^2$, there is an extra peak in the spectrum due to the ionisation of an unpaired electron in an orbital of 85% $V(3d)$ character. According to the *ab initio* calculations mentioned above, this orbital is of e symmetry, and its ionisation energy is 9·41 eV. Since the molecular ground state is a doublet, the ionisation of the orbitals above 9·41 eV produces both singlet and triplet states, but the resultant structure has not been resolved. These deeper orbitals are expected to ionise in the same order as in CCl_4 and $TiCl_4$.

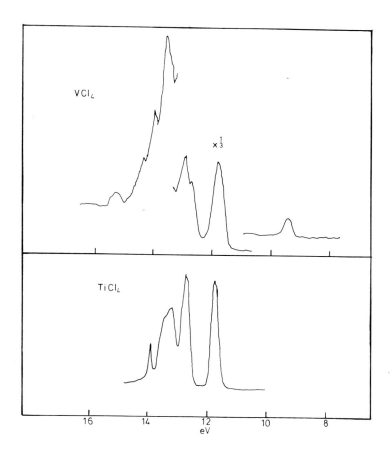

Figure 70.1. The photoelectron spectra of $TiCl_4$ and VCl_4 obtained using He(I) radiation (Cox *et al* 1970).

The engagement of the metallic electrons in the largely halogenic orbitals introduced earlier in this chapter causes the polarisation M^+–Cl^-. There is a considerable fall in energy; the VOIE of V(3d) is 6·3 eV and the origin of the chemical stability is here. The orbitals of Cl_4 interacting with the metal also fall in energy. Another source of chemical stability in VCl_4 is the mixing of the orbital carrying the unpaired electron with the unoccupied orbitals of Cl_4 which are not far away in energy. This is sometimes called 'back-bonding'.

Isoelectronic with $TiCl_4$ is CrO_2Cl_2, a deep red liquid which boils at 117 °C. The decrease in symmetry from T_d to the C_{2v} point group leads to the raising of the

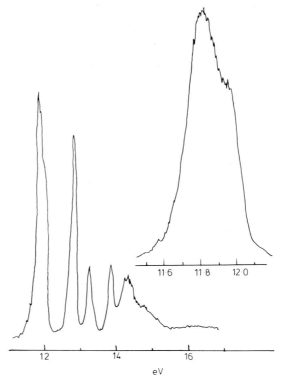

Figure 70.2. The photoelectron spectrum of CrO_2Cl_2 obtained using He(I) radiation (Lee and Rabalais 1975).

degeneracy of the orbitals;

$$e \rightarrow a_1 + a_2$$

$$t_1 \rightarrow a_2 + b_1 + b_2$$

$$t_2 \rightarrow a_1 + b_1 + b_2.$$

Table 70.1. Ionisation energies (Cox *et al* 1970, Green *et al* 1970, Lee and Rabalais 1975) of transition metal halides. There is doubt about some of these values since they refer to shoulders in the spectra rather than well resolved peaks.

	a_1	$t_2(\pi)$	e	$t_2(\sigma)$	t_1	e
$TiCl_4$	13·97	13·4	13·23	12·78	11·78	—
				11·7		
$TiBr_4$	13·08	12·4	12·25	11·8	10·56	—
				12·0	10·80	
VCl_4	15·26	13·9	13·54	12·88	11·75	9·41
CrO_2Cl_2†	14·8	13·8	13·2	12·7	11·8	—

† The point group of CrO_2Cl_2 is C_{2v} and the symmetries are therefore not those of the heading in this case.

The spectrum of CrO_2Cl_2 is given in figure 70·2, and the ionisation energies of transition metal halides are set out in table 70.1.

71 Ruthenium and Osmium Tetroxides

Two solid forms of RuO_4 are known; a colourless one, which melts at 25·5 °C, and a brown one which melts at 27 °C. The vapour is unstable and sometimes explodes on heating, leaving the dioxide, RuO_2. Osmium tetroxide is a yellow solid which melts at 40·6 °C and boils at 129 °C. Both oxides are volatile and sublime readily. Ruthenium tetroxide has been found to be very reactive in the spectrometer and causes a deterioration of the instrument (Foster *et al* 1973). The photoelectron spectra of RuO_4 and OsO_4 are shown in figure 71.1.

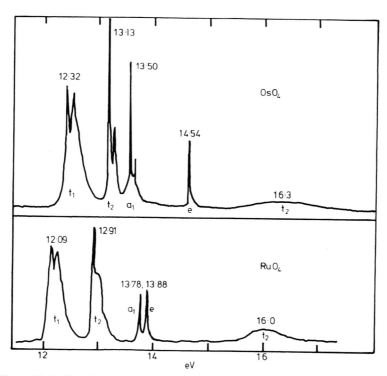

Figure 71.1. The photoelectron spectra of ruthenium and osmium tetroxides (Foster *et al* 1973); only tentative assignments are given (Weber 1977).

These tetroxides are isoelectronic with CCl_4, $TiCl_4$, etc, discussed in the preceeding sections. The central atoms have the valence configuration d^6s^2, and it is noted that there are twice as many electrons from the central atom as in $TiCl_4$. The valence orbital ionisation energies are 5·81 eV (Ru_{5s}), 9·66 eV (Ru_{4d}), 6·02 eV (Os_{6s}) and 9·42 eV (Os_{5d}).

In both compounds the O–O separation distance is about 3 Å. The σ overlap integral for O(2p) at this distance is only 0·007 and the interaction between the O atoms is therefore quite small; the calculated separation between the energy levels of O_4 is less than 1 eV. Calculations of different authors have not always agreed as to the ordering of the ionisation energies (Foster *et al* 1973, Weber 1977).

The one-electron spin–orbit coupling constants of Ru and Os are approximately 0·12 eV and 0·37 eV, respectively. Since the $t_2(\pi)$ orbital is expected to have perhaps $\frac{1}{3}$ central atom component, a spin–orbit splitting of about 0·1 eV is anticipated in OsO_4. Unfortunately there are vibrational progressions of about the same interval in the bands, and spin–orbit interaction has not been observed with certainty.

72   Nickel Tetracarbonyl

$Ni(CO)_4$ is a colourless liquid which melts at $-25\,°C$ and boils at $43\,°C$. The Ni—C bond is sufficiently weak for there to be an equilibrium in the gas phase;

$$Ni(CO)_4 \rightarrow Ni + 4CO.$$

The 5σ orbitals of CO (figure 47.1) are analogous to p–σ orbitals in the Cl_4 tetrahedron spanning t_2 and a_1. The C–C distance is 3·15 Å and the C(2p) Slater overlap integral, S_σ, at this distance is 0·04, compared with 0·06 for the corresponding integral in CCl_4.

The 1π orbitals of CO span t_1, e and t_2 (compare the 1e orbital of the methyl radical in figure 69.1) but the carbonyl orbitals mentioned are fully occupied;

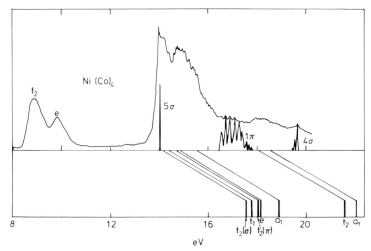

Figure 72.1. The photoelectron spectrum of $Ni(CO)_4$ (Hillier *et al* 1974). Some CO is present and its spectrum is included; the peaks are labelled 5σ, 1π and 4σ. The peaks labelled t_2 and e are of mainly Ni(3d) composition. Energy eigenvalues calculated by an SCF method (Demuynk and Veillard 1973) are indicated.

hence the metallic electrons do not complete the occupation of the orbitals of the ligand tetrahedron in $Ni(CO)_4$ as they do in the tetramethyls and the other molecules discussed previously in this chapter.

In the spectrum in figure 72.1, the bands attributable to the ligands lie at much the same energies as in free CO. The amount of metal character in the corresponding orbitals has been calculated by an *ab initio* method (Hillier and Saunders 1971) as follows: 23% (t_2, σ), 0% (t_1), 4% (e), 2% (t_2, π) and 1% (a_1). Although these values are imprecise they indicate that there is sigma interaction between the ligands and the central atom.

The valence electrons of Ni (configuration $3d^8 4s^2$) occupy orbitals of t_2 and e symmetry in $Ni(CO)_4$, and ionise at 8·9 and 9·77 eV, respectively. These assignments are based upon the relative intensities of the bands and *ab initio* calculations indicating 74% metallic character for t_2 and 90% for e (Hillier and Saunders 1971). Opinion differs as to the relative importance of sigma interaction and back-bonding in $Ni(CO)_4$. According to a recent calculation (Baerends and Ros 1975), π back-donation is the more important and has the effect of placing about one half of an electronic charge in the antibonding 2π orbitals of the CO ligands, whereas sigma donation places about one-quarter of a charge in the Ni(4p) orbital. Both effects lower the strength of the C—O bond.

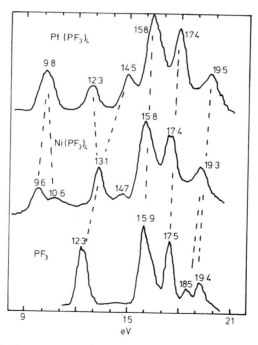

Figure 73.1. Photoelectron spectra of PF_3 and its complexes with Ni and Pt (Hillier *et al* 1970). There is some doubt about the existence of the 14·7 eV peak of the Ni complex.

73   Trifluorophosphine Complexes, Ni(PF₃)₄ and Pt(PF₃)₄

Trifluorophosphine, PF_3, is a colourless gas. Its bonding orbitals are all occupied and its complexes with metals can be likened to that of carbon monoxide. Electron diffraction studies in the gas phase show that the geometry of the PF_3 ligand is not greatly changed from that of the free molecule and that it undergoes free rotation about the metal–phosphorus bond in $Ni(PF_3)_4$ (Marriot *et al* 1970, Almenningen *et al* 1970).

In figure 73.1 the photoelectron spectrum of the free ligand is given. The spectra of $Ni(PF_3)_4$ and $Pt(PF_3)_4$, which are also given in the figure, contain peaks that appear to be very similar to those of the free ligand. The lowest of these is the sigma orbital (symmetry a_1 in C_{3v}), which is largely a phosphorus lone pair. As in $Ni(CO)_4$, π back-bonding is important but it could be that PF_3 is a more efficient π acceptor than is CO, since the metal ionisation energies are higher in $Ni(PF_3)_4$ than in $Ni(CO)_4$.

Problems

1   Derive the orbital numbered 8 in table 64.2 from that numbered 7 by a threefold rotation. Show that a further threefold rotation regenerates orbital number 6. Show that these orbitals transform as t_1 in the T_d point group and that they are orthogonal and normalised.

2   Find the average energy of the eigenvalues given in table 65.2. Show that the average energies of the two sets of orbitals (those derived from p orbitals of π and σ symmetry) are the same.

3   Show that a tetrahedral disposition of s orbitals spans the same set of irreducible representations as the sigma p orbitals discussed in § 63. Derive the wavefunctions of the s-derived molecular orbitals and hence the energies in terms of the integral, γ, of § 67.

4 B_4Cl_4 can be derived from the tetrahedral array of four BCl units with the B—Cl axis directed towards the centre. Elucidate the molecular orbitals of BCl that will be involved and work out what irreducible representations they span. Can you say *a priori* whether BCl would be stable? In fact, BCl_3 is the stable chloride.

5   In table 69.1 the ionisation energies of the group IV tetramethyls are given. Show that the average of the energies labelled $3t_2$ and $2a_1$ is close to $11 \cdot 7$ eV, the calculated energy of the $2a_1$ orbital of methyl. Similarly, show that the average of $1t_2$, $1e$ and $2t_2$ is close to the value for $1e$ (methyl), $13 \cdot 9$ eV. Explain why this should be so.

10 Octahedral Molecules

74 Octahedrally Disposed p Orbitals

The discussion of Chapter 9 concerned the problem of the tetrahedral disposition of twelve p orbitals. In this chapter, in the same spirit, attention is directed towards octahedral geometry involving eighteen p orbitals (figure 74.1). The point group is

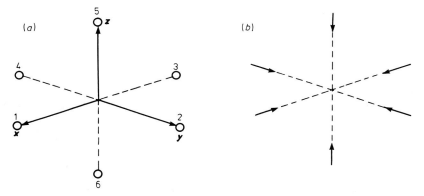

Figure 74.1. Octahedral geometry showing (a) the axes and the numbering of the atoms, and (b) the direction of the sigma orbitals. The latter are seen to be $-x_1$, $-y_2$, x_3, y_4, $-z_5$ and z_6.

O_h (table 74.1) and the p orbitals can be subdivided in the same way as in the last chapter; those pointing directly at the centre are called σ orbitals and those pointing perpendicularly to the σ orbitals are called π orbitals. The σ orbitals span a_{1g}, e_g and

Table 74.1. Character table of the O_h point group.

O_h	E	$8C_3$	$6C_2$	$6C_4$	$3C_2=C_4^2$	i	$6S_4$	$8S_6$	$3\sigma_h$	$6\sigma_d$	
A_{1g}	1	1	1	1	1	1	1	1	1	1	$x^2+y^2+z^2$
A_{2g}	1	1	−1	−1	1	1	−1	1	1	−1	
E_g	2	−1	0	0	2	2	0	−1	2	0	$\begin{cases} 2z^2-x^2-y^2 \\ x^2-y^2 \end{cases}$
T_{1g}	3	0	−1	1	−1	3	1	0	−1	−1	R_x, R_y, R_z
T_{2g}	3	0	1	−1	−1	3	−1	0	−1	1	xy, yz, zx
A_{1u}	1	1	1	1	1	−1	−1	−1	−1	−1	
A_{2u}	1	1	−1	−1	1	−1	1	−1	−1	1	xyz
E_u	2	−1	0	0	2	−2	0	1	−2	0	
T_{1u}	3	0	−1	1	−1	−3	−1	0	1	1	x, y, z
T_{2u}	3	0	1	−1	−1	−3	1	0	1	−1	

t_{1u}, and the wavefunctions are

$$a_{1g} = \frac{1}{\sqrt{6}}(-x_1 - y_2 + x_3 + y_4 - z_5 + z_6)$$

$$e_g = \tfrac{1}{2}(-x_1 + y_2 + x_3 - y_4), \text{ etc}$$

$$t_{1u} = \frac{1}{\sqrt{2}}(x_1 + x_3), \text{ etc.}$$

The π orbitals span t_{1u}, t_{2g}, t_{1g} and t_{2u}, and examples of their wavefunctions are

$$t_{1u} = \tfrac{1}{2}(x_2 + x_4 + x_5 + x_6)$$

$$t_{2g} = \tfrac{1}{2}(z_1 - z_3 + x_5 - x_6)$$

$$t_{1g} = \tfrac{1}{2}(z_1 - x_5 - z_3 + x_6)$$

$$t_{2u} = \tfrac{1}{2}(x_2 + x_4 - x_5 - x_6).$$

These orbitals are illustrated in figure 74.2. They have been normalised on the assumption that the overlap integrals are zero and that the atomic orbitals are normalised already. In terms of the empirical parameters used in Chapter 9, the energy of the a_{1g} orbital is found to be

$$\alpha + 4A + \sigma'$$

where α is the usual Coulomb integral, A is the resonance integral between orbitals with the same relative orientation as between x_1 and y_2, and σ' is the resonance integral between orbitals x_1 and $-x_3$, etc. Resolution of the vectors of the A integral into their π and their σ components shows that

$$A = \tfrac{1}{2}\pi + \tfrac{1}{2}\sigma$$

where σ is the integral between adjacent (*cis*) p orbitals pointing directly at each other in collinear fashion, and π is the integral for adjacent p orbitals in the pi orientation. Hence the energies of the molecular orbitals derived from the sigma atomic orbitals are

$$a_{1g} = \alpha + 2\pi + 2\sigma + 2\sigma'$$

$$e_g = \alpha - \pi - \sigma + \sigma'$$

$$t_{1u} = \alpha - \sigma'.$$

For the molecular orbitals derived from the π atomic orbitals, it is necessary to define another integral, denoted π', which is analogous to σ'. π' is the resonance integral between, for example, z_2 and z_4, that is, between the *trans* p orbitals of π orientation. The energies are easily shown to be

$$t_{1u} = \alpha + 2\pi + \pi'$$

$$t_{2g} = \alpha + \pi + \sigma - \pi'$$

$$t_{1g} = \alpha - \pi - \sigma - \pi'$$

$$t_{2u} = \alpha - 2\pi + \pi'.$$

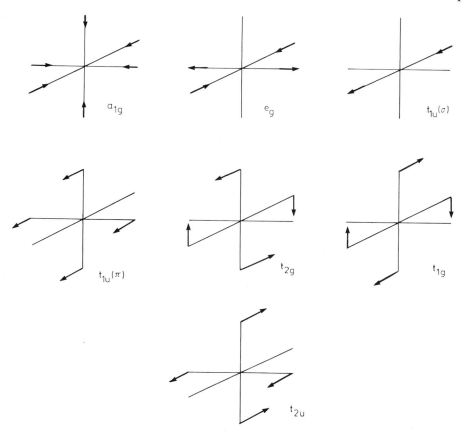

Figure 74.2. Arrangements of octahedrally disposed p orbitals transforming according to the irreducible representations of the O_h point group.

The integrals between *trans* atomic orbitals, π' and σ', are found to be of negligible magnitude for our purposes. In SF_6, for example, the overlap integrals between the Slater F(2p) orbitals are 0·021 (σ), 0·003 (π) and less than 10^{-4} for σ' and π'.

75 Hexafluorides

SF_6 is a gas of remarkable stability, which is unaffected by fused alkalis, halogens at less than red heat, and molten sodium. SeF_6 has a similar stability, but TeF_6 is hydrolysed by water. The central atoms of the foregoing have the s^2p^4 configuration but when the configuration is s^2d^4, as in MoF_6 and WF_6, there is a high degree of reactivity. This also applies to UF_6, where the metal configuration may possibly be $5f^36d^17s^2$, the three atomic orbitals here being close in energy. MoF_6, WF_6 and UF_6 are all very reactive towards water; MoF_6 attacks metals and UF_6 reacts vigorously with organic materials. All are sufficiently volatile for the measurement of their spectra in the gas phase, the boiling points being $-64\,°C$ (sublimation, SF_6),

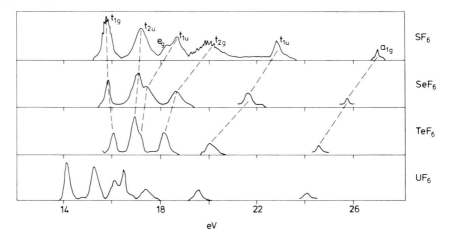

Figure 75.1. The photoelectron spectra of UF_6 and the group VI hexafluorides (Potts *et al* 1970). The SF_6 spectrum was obtained with light of energy 40·8 eV, and the others with light of energy 21·21 eV. The use of 21·21 eV light in the case of SF_6 gave a different intensity distribution, which may be attributable to autoionisation.

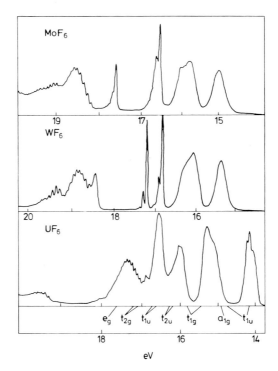

Figure 75.2. The photoelectron spectra of MoF_6, WF_6 and UF_6 (Siegbahn 1975) obtained with light of 21·21 eV energy.

−46·6 °C (SeF$_6$), −39 °C (TeF$_6$), 35 °C (MoF$_6$), 17·5 °C (WF$_6$) and 56·5 °C (sublimation, UF$_6$). Chemical reactivity increases with molecular dimensions, the M–F
distances being 1·56 Å (SF$_6$), 1·7 Å (SeF$_6$), 1·82 Å (TeF$_6$) and 2·4 Å (UF$_6$). Estimated values are 1·98 Å (MoF$_6$) and 2·04 Å (WF$_6$). In UF$_6$ the corresponding σ
overlap integral is only 0·07, which is about a third of its value in SF$_6$.

The photoelectron spectra of SF$_6$, SeF$_6$ and TeF$_6$ are much alike (figure 75·1).
There is also a superficial resemblance to the spectrum of UF$_6$, but in view of the
differences between this spectrum and those of MoF$_6$ and WF$_6$ (figure 75.2), it
would appear to be unwise to conclude that a similar situation prevails throughout.

From the results of § 74 the ordering of ionisation potentials of the orbitals of the
F$_6$ octahedron is apparently e$_g$ = t$_{1g}$ < t$_{2u}$ < t$_{1u}(\sigma)$ < t$_{1u}(\pi)$ < t$_{2g}$ < a$_{1g}$ (figure 75.3). It
is to be anticipated that the two orbitals of the t$_{1u}$ irreducible representation will
mix together and shift apart in energy. The orbitals of the central atom span a$_{1g}$ (s
orbitals), t$_{1u}$ (p orbitals), e$_g$ + t$_{2g}$ (d orbitals) and a$_{2u}$ + t$_{1u}$ + t$_{2u}$ (f orbitals).

A number of SCF calculations agree (von Niessen *et al* 1975) that the e$_g$ orbital of
SF$_6$ is lowered in energy by interaction with S(3d), although the valence orbital
ionisation energies of F(2p) and S(3d) differ substantially (figure 75.3). It seems
safe, therefore, to conclude that the orbital of lowest ionisation energy is t$_{1g}$. In the
absence of a nearby f orbital, the orbital of t$_{2u}$ designation is likely to be the next in

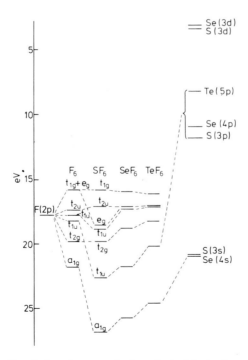

Figure 75.3. Correlations between the hypothetical ionisation energies of the F$_6$
octahedron and the ionisation energies of the group VI hexafluorides. Opinion with
regard to the assignments differs (von Niessen *et al* 1975).

line of ionisation; von Niessen *et al* (1975) calculate it to have about the same ionisation energy as the upper t_{1u}. Mixing together of the t_{1u} orbitals of F_6 is anticipated not only to cause them to shift apart in energy, but also to lose to some extent their designations as σ and π. In SF_6 the S(3p)–F(2p) overlap integrals are 0·23 (σ), 0·10 (π) and the S(3s)–F(2p) overlap is 0·17, these values being calculated with Slater orbitals. Clearly, σ interaction is of prime importance, and the lowering of a_{1g} and t_{1u} orbitals in figure 75.3 is in accordance with their expected interaction with S(3s) and S(3p). The t_{2g} orbital of the F_6 octahedron appears to interact very little with S(3d), presumably on account of the large energy separation and the π character of t_{2g}.

Reasons for the chemical stability of SF_6 are not hard to find. The electrons of the central atom complete the set required to fill the orbitals of the F_6 group (there is an analogy here with CF_4), and the overlap integrals between the orbitals of the central atom and the F atoms are substantial.

Recent relativistic calculations (Rosén 1978) have shown that in UF_6 there is a considerable spin–orbit interaction giving rise to the splittings,

$$t_2 = e_{1/2} + g_{3/2}$$

$$t_2 = e_{5/2} + g_{3/2}.$$

The assignments resulting from these calculations are shown in figure 75.2.

76　Hexacarbonyls

The hexacarbonyls of Cr, Mo and W are white, crystalline solids which sublime easily; their spectra are given in figure 76.1. The chemical bonding is similar to that of $Ni(CO)_4$ discussed in § 72, but instead of ten d electrons there are only six, and these fill a set of orbitals of t_{2g} symmetry; peaks due to their ionisation are found at 8·4 eV in $Cr(CO)_6$, 8·5 eV in $Mo(CO)_6$ and 8·56 eV in $W(CO)_6$. As pointed out in § 72 these largely metallic orbitals also contain a contribution from the antibonding and otherwise unoccupied $CO(2\pi)$ orbitals, giving rise to 'back-bonding'. Partial occupation of the antibonding CO orbitals in this fashion causes a diminution in the C—O bond strength, which is evidenced by a fall in the stretching frequency.

According to a number of calculations the ionisation next in the spectrum after the metallic t_{2g} peak is that of the mainly ligand t_{1u} orbital (Baerends and Ros 1975). The corresponding band stands well clear (figure 76.1), but the following ones are too close together to be assigned with confidence.

$V(CO)_6$ contains only five d electrons and the corresponding band in the spectrum possesses incipient structure, a pair of peaks at 7·52 eV and 7·88 eV being just discernible (Evans *et al* 1969). This structure arises from the states of the t_{2g}^4 configuration of the ion. Since it is equivalent to a pair of 'holes' in the t_{2g} shell, this configuration spans the irreducible representations of the direct product, $t_{2g} \times t_{2g} = a_{1g} + e_g + t_{2g} + t_{1g}$. Of these, only t_{1g} is antisymmetric, producing a triplet state, $^3T_{1g}$.

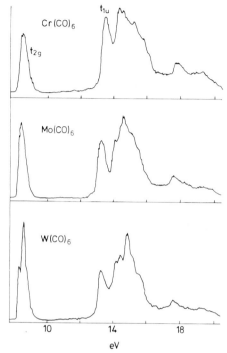

Figure 76.1. The photoelectron spectra of the hexacarbonyls, obtained with light of 21·21 eV energy (Higginson *et al* 1973).

The others give singlet states (§ 43). The expected relative intensities of the corresponding peaks in the spectrum are given by the overall spin–orbit degeneracies; $1:2:3:9$ for $^1A_{1g}$, ^1E_g, $^1T_{2g}$ and $^3T_{1g}$, respectively, but the poor resolution precludes a test of this prediction.

77 Hexatrifluorophosphine Complexes

The complexes of Ni and Pt were discussed in § 73, and the octahedral complexes of Cr, Mo and W discussed here are similar in most respects. Thermal stability is greater than among the carbonyls, possibly on account of the enhanced properties of the PF_3 ligand with regard to back-donation. Evidence for this is an increase in ionisation energy with respect to the carbonyls of the metallic t_{2g} orbital. This increase amounts to about 0·9 eV. Observed band maxima are 9·29 eV in $Cr(PF_3)_6$, 9·17 eV in $Mo(PF_3)_6$ and 9·3 eV in $W(PF_3)_6$.

From the discussions of §§ 73 and 74 it might be expected that there would be three bands in the spectrum derived from the ionisation of the mainly ligand (sigma) t_{1u}, e_g and a_{1g} orbitals. In the absence of nearby f orbitals the t_{1u} orbital should ionise at about the same energy as in PF_3 itself, that is, at 12·3 eV. There is a

Photoelectron Spectroscopy and Molecular Orbitals

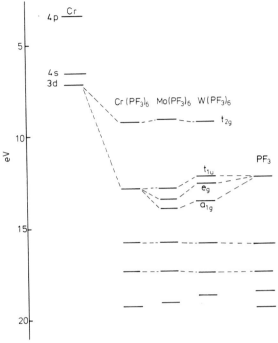

Figure 77.1. Correlation diagram for the ionisation energies of the trifluoro-phosphine complexes of Cr, Mo and W. The ionisation energies of PF_3 are included.

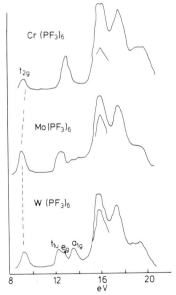

Figure 77.2. The spectra of the octahedral complexes of trifluorophosphine (Head *et al* 1975).

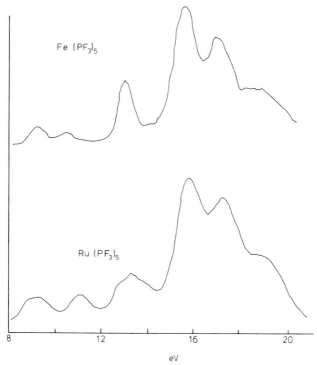

Figure 77.3. The spectra of Fe(PF$_3$)$_5$ and Ru(PF$_3$)$_5$, obtained using light of 21·21 eV energy (Head *et al* 1975).

peak at 12·26 eV in the spectrum of W(PF$_3$)$_6$ that can therefore be assigned as t_{1u} (figures 77.1 and 77.2). The e_g orbital is lowered in ionisation energy by ligand–ligand interactions, which are probably small and raised by interactions with the metal d orbitals; it probably comes next in the spectrum. The a_{1g} orbital is bonding on both counts and is therefore assigned the last place. In Cr(PF$_3$)$_6$ the three bands have merged together.

The other peaks in the spectra of the Cr, W and Mo hexatrifluorophosphine complexes are clearly identifiable with peaks in the spectra of the free ligand (figure 73.1).

The valence shells of Fe and Ru possess a pair of electrons extra to those of Cr, Mo and W. The extra electrons can be imagined to replace one PF$_3$ lone pair and the complexes have the formula M(PF$_3$)$_5$. Assuming that the geometry is that of the trigonal bipyramid (point group D$_{3h}$), the d orbitals span e″, e′ and a$_1'$. The ionisation of the e″ and e′ orbitals produces two peaks which are visible in the spectra (figure 77.3).

Problems

1 Derive the energies of the orbitals given in § 74 and show that the average energy is α. Verify that the orbitals have the symmetries indicated.

2   On the basis of the diagram in figure 75.3 predict an approximate spectrum for SCl_6. What further complications would you anticipate in SI_6?

3   In the spectrum of $Cr(CO)_5NH_3$ the lowest ionisation energies are those of a pair of peaks lying at 7·56 and 7·85 eV. How do you account for these?

Appendix I   Physical Constants

	Working unit	SI unit
Velocity of light	$c = 2 \cdot 998 \times 10^{10}$ cm s^{-1}	$2 \cdot 998 \times 10^8$ m s^{-1}
Charge of electron	$e = 4 \cdot 803 \times 10^{-10}$ esu	$1 \cdot 602 \times 10^{-19}$ C
Mass of electron	$m = 9 \cdot 109 \times 10^{-28}$ g	$9 \cdot 109 \times 10^{-31}$ kg
Mass of proton	$1 \cdot 673 \times 10^{-24}$ g	$1 \cdot 673 \times 10^{-27}$ kg
Planck's constant	$h = 6 \cdot 626 \times 10^{-27}$ erg s	$6 \cdot 626 \times 10^{-34}$ J s
Avogadro's number	$6 \cdot 023 \times 10^{23}$ mol^{-1}	$6 \cdot 023 \times 10^{23}$ mol^{-1}
Rydberg's constant	$R = 13 \cdot 595$ eV	$2 \cdot 180 \times 10^{-18}$ J
Bohr radius $[h^2/(4\pi^2 me^2)]$	$a_0 = 0 \cdot 5292$ Å	
Permittivity of free space		$\epsilon_0 = 8 \cdot 854 \times 10^{-12}$ F m^{-1}
Permeability of free space		$\mu_0 = 4\pi \times 10^{-7}$ N A^{-2}

1 electron volt (eV) $= 1 \cdot 602 \times 10^{-12}$ erg/molecule
$= 23 \cdot 05$ kcal mol^{-1}
$= 8068$ cm^{-1}
$= 1 \cdot 602 \times 10^{-19}$ J
$= 0 \cdot 0376$ atomic units (au)
$= 96 \cdot 49$ kJ mol^{-1}
1 atomic unit $(e^2/a_0) = 27 \cdot 21$ eV
1 ångström unit (Å) $= 10^{-8}$ cm

Appendix II   The Greek Alphabet

A, α	. . . . . Alpha		N, ν	. . . . . Nu
B, β	. . . . . Beta		Ξ, ξ	 Xi
Γ, γ	. . . . . Gamma		O, o	. . . . . Omicron
Δ, δ	. . . . . Delta		Π, π	. . . . . Pi
E, ϵ	. . . . . Epsilon		P, ρ	. . . . . Rho
Z, ζ	. . . . . Zeta		Σ, σ	. . . . . Sigma
H, η	. . . . . Eta		T, τ	. . . . . Tau
Θ, ϑ, θ	. . . . Theta		Υ, υ	. . . . . Upsilon
I, ι	. . . . . Iota		Φ, φ, ϕ	. . . Phi
K, κ	. . . . . Kappa		X, χ	. . . . . Chi
Λ, λ	. . . . . Lambda		Ψ, ψ	. . . . . Psi
M, μ	. . . . Mu		Ω, ω	. . . . . Omega

Appendix III Valence Orbital Ionisation Energies

The ionisation energy of an atomic orbital depends on the configuration and the state; for example, for carbon in the $1s^2 2s^2 2p^2$ configuration, we have either the ^1S, ^1D or ^3P state. In a molecule the configuration and state of the free atom lose significance; for example, in the transition metals where the valence d and s

Table AIII.1. Valence orbital ionisation energies (in eV).

	1s	2s	2p	3s	3p	4s	4p	3d	5s	5p
H	13·6									
He	24·5									
Li		5·5								
Be		9·3								
B		14·0	8·3							
C		19·5	10·7							
N		25·5	13·1							
O		32·4	15·9							
F		46·4	18·7							
Ne		48·5	21·6							
Na				5·2						
Mg				7·7						
Al				11·3	5·9					
Si				15·0	7·8					
P				18·7	10·2					
S				20·7	11·7					
Cl				25·3	13·8					
Ar				29·3	15·9					
K						4·3				
Ca						6·1				
Zn						9·4				
Ga						12·6	5·9			
Ge						15·6	7·6			
As						17·6	9·0			
Se						20·8	10·8			
Br						24·0	12·5			
Kr						27·5	14·3			
I									20·8	11·2
Sc						5·7	3·2	4·7		
Ti						6·1	3·3	5·6		
V						6·3	3·5	6·3		
Cr						6·6	3·5	7·2		
Mn						6·8	3·6	7·9		
Fe						7·1	3·7	8·7		
Co						7·3	3·8	9·4		
Ni						7·6	3·8	10·0		
Cu						7·7	4·0	10·7		

energies are close. An average ionisation energy taken over the available configurations and states called the *valence orbital ionisation energy* (VOIE), is useful. For example, the diagonal matrix element H_{ii} is often equated with the VOIE of the ith atom.

As an example, let us calculate the VOIE of the 2p orbitals of $C(1s^2 2s^2 2p^2)$. The lowest ionisation energy is 11·264 eV, according to Moore's tables, and the energies of the states of the ground configuration are 2·683 eV (^1S), 1·263 eV (^1D) and 0·021 eV (^3P). The ion has only the ^2P state. The degeneracies of the ^1S, ^1D and ^3P states are 1, 5 and 9, respectively, and the average energy of the p^2 configuration is therefore 0·601 eV. The VOIE is the ionisation energy plus the average energy of the ionic configuration, minus the average energy of the ground configuration, which is $11·264 - 0·601 = 10·663$ eV. For $I(5s)$ the average energy of $5s^2 5p^5$ is 0·31 eV and the average of $5s^1 5p^5$ is 10·69 eV. The ionisation energy of 5s is 10·45 eV and the VOIE is $10·45 + 10·69 - 0·31 = 20·8$ eV.

Further values are given in table AIII.1. Where necessary, these were obtained by interpolation since for some elements the required data are not available.

Appendix IV   Symmetric and Antisymmetric Wavefunctions

Suppose that there are two wavefunctions, $\underline{a}$ and $\underline{b}$. If there are electrons numbered 1 and 2 in these orbitals we can write them either $\underline{a}_1$ and $\underline{b}_2$ or $\underline{a}_2$ and $\underline{b}_1$. The total wavefunction of the system could be either $\psi = \underline{a}_1\underline{b}_2$ or $\psi = \underline{a}_2\underline{b}_1$ but, according to the Pauli principle, all electronic wavefunctions must be antisymmetric with respect to the exchange of electrons, and we write

$$\psi = \underline{a}_1\underline{b}_2 - \underline{a}_2\underline{b}_1.$$

In group theory we can divide representations into symmetric and antisymmetric classes as follows.

Suppose that the functions $\underline{a}_1 \ldots \underline{a}_f$ constitute an irreducible representation of species A and the functions $\underline{b}_1 \ldots \underline{b}_g$ comprise another of species B. The direct product of the two is $(\underline{a}_1 \ldots \underline{a}_f) \times (\underline{b}_1 \ldots \underline{b}_g) = \ldots \underline{a}_i\underline{b}_j \ldots$, and a set of new functions, fg in number, form the basis of a new representation which is generally reducible.

The effect of a symmetry operation, $\hat{G}$, upon $\underline{a}_i$, for example, is to produce a combination of the other functions of the same basis,

$$\hat{G}\underline{a}_i = \sum_j G_{ij}\underline{a}_j.$$

Acting upon all the $\underline{a}_i$ functions in this manner produces a matrix of G_{ij} of the order f^2. The character of the representation made up of the $\underline{a}_i$ functions under the operation $\hat{G}$ is the sum of the diagonal terms of the matrix (the trace of the matrix)

$$\chi^a(\hat{G}) = \sum_i G_{ii}^a.$$

The character, $\chi^a(\hat{G})$, can be thought of as the sum of component $\underline{a}$ functions unchanged by the operation.

The character of the direct product is the product of the pair of component characters

$$(\chi^a \times \chi^b) = \sum_i G_{ii}^a \sum_j G_{jj}^b.$$

If the two irreducible representations are the same, the direct product can be divided into symmetric and antisymmetric classes. The new functions of the form $\underline{a}_i\underline{b}_j$ are $f^2 = fg$ in number and can be subdivided thus;

$$\ldots \underline{a}_i\underline{b}_j \ldots = \tfrac{1}{2}(\underline{a}_i\underline{b}_j + \underline{a}_j\underline{b}_i) + \tfrac{1}{2}(\underline{a}_i\underline{b}_j - \underline{a}_j\underline{b}_i).$$

The first term on the right is symmetric and the second is antisymmetric. The character of the symmetric direct product is derived as follows;

$$\hat{G}(\underline{a}_i\underline{b}_j) = \sum_m G_{im}\underline{a}_m \sum_n G_{jn}\underline{b}_n,$$

and in order to obtain the symmetric term we need,

$$(G_{ii}\underline{a}_i)(G_{jj}\underline{b}_j) + (G_{ij}\underline{a}_j)(G_{ji}\underline{b}_i).$$

Hence the character of the symmetric direct product is the sum

$$\tfrac{1}{2}(G_{ii}G_{jj} + G_{ij}G_{ji}) = \tfrac{1}{2}\{\chi^2(\hat{G}) + \chi(\hat{G}^2)\}.$$

Similarly, for the antisymmetric part of the direct product the character is

$$\tfrac{1}{2}\{\chi^2(G) - \chi(G^2)\}.$$

As an example, consider the $D_{\infty h}$ point group. The characters of π_g are set out below.

	E	C^ϕ	σ_v	i	S^ϕ	C_2
$\chi(\hat{G})$	2	$2\cos\phi$	0	2	$-2\cos\phi$	0
$\chi^2(\hat{G})$	4	$4\cos^2\phi$	0	4	$4\cos^2\phi$	0
$\chi(\hat{G}^2)$	2	$2\cos 2\phi$	2	2	$2\cos 2\phi$	2

Noting that $4\cos^2\phi = 2 + 2\cos 2\phi$, the characters of the symmetric product are found to be

$$3 \quad (1+\cos 2\phi) \quad 1 \quad 3 \quad (1+\cos 2\phi) \quad 1$$

which is the sum of the characters of $\Sigma_g^+ + \Delta_g$. For the antisymmetric product the result is Σ_g^-.

Appendix V   The Raising and Lowering Operators

Equation (5.5) can easily be generalised to give the other components of orbital angular momentum: for example,

$$\hat{M}_x = \frac{-ih}{2\pi}(y\,d/dz - z\,d/dy).$$

These operators fail to commute with one another; for example,

$$\hat{M}_y\hat{M}_z - \hat{M}_z\hat{M}_y = \frac{ih}{2\pi}\hat{M}_x \qquad\qquad (AV.1)$$

$$\hat{M}_z\hat{M}_x - \hat{M}_x\hat{M}_z = \frac{ih}{2\pi}\hat{M}_y. \qquad\qquad (AV.2)$$

It is easy to prove the unlikely looking result

$$\hat{M}_z(\hat{M}_x \pm i\hat{M}_y) = (\hat{M}_x \pm i\hat{M}_y)\left(\hat{M}_z \pm \frac{h}{2\pi}\right)$$

by expanding the left-hand side with equations (AV.1) and (AV.2). Writing $\hat{M}_+$ for $\hat{M}_x + i\hat{M}_y$ and $\hat{M}_-$ for $\hat{M}_x - i\hat{M}_y$,

$$\hat{M}_z\hat{M}_\pm = \hat{M}_\pm\left(\hat{M}_z \pm \frac{h}{2\pi}\right).$$

$\hat{M}_+$ and $\hat{M}_-$ are known as the raising (or step-up) and the lowering (or step-down) operators, respectively. Consideration of equation (6.6) helps to explain these epithets, because the above result can only mean that $\hat{M}_+$ raises the value of m by unity, whilst M_- decreases m by the same amount. Thus a function $\phi(l, m, s, m_s)$ becomes $\phi(l, m+1, s, m_s)$ when operated upon by $\hat{M}_+$;

$$\hat{M}_+\phi(l, m, s, m_s) = A\phi(l, m+1, s, m_s)$$

and

$$\hat{M}_-\phi(l, m, s, m_s) = B\phi(l, m-1, s, m_s).$$

In order to discover the eigenvalues A and B we note that

$$\hat{M}_+^2 = \hat{M}_x^2 + i(\hat{M}_x\hat{M}_y - \hat{M}_y\hat{M}_x) + \hat{M}_y^2$$

$$= \hat{M}_x^2 - \frac{h}{2\pi}\hat{M}_z + \hat{M}_y^2$$

$$= \hat{M}^2 - \hat{M}_z^2 - \frac{h}{2\pi}\hat{M}_z.$$

The eigenvalue of the last is

$$\{l(l+1)-m^2-m\}\{h/(2\pi)\}^2 = (l+m+1)(l-m)\{h/(2\pi)\}^2$$

and the final result is

$$\hat{M}_\pm\phi(l,\,m,\,s,\,m_s) = [(l\pm m+1)(l\mp m)]^{1/2}\{h/(2\pi)\}\phi(l,\,m\pm 1,\,s,\,m_s).$$

Exactly similar expressions hold for spin; for example,

$$\hat{S}_+ = \hat{S}_x + i\hat{S}_y$$

and

$$\hat{S}_\pm\phi(l,\,m,\,s,\,m_s) = [(s\pm m_s+1)(s\mp m)]^{1/2}\{h/(2\pi)\}\phi(l,\,m,\,s,\,m_s\pm 1).$$

Appendix VI Spin–Orbit Interaction Between $\psi(^3\Sigma_g^-)$ and $\psi(^1\Sigma_g^+)$ of O_2

In § 43 the wavefunctions of the states of the configuration π_g^2 were given for O_2 and congeners. Because it is a nuclear property, spin–orbit interaction is dependent on the atomic functions comprising the molecular functions, and it is necessary to analyse, for example, equation (43.1) into its atomic components. This particular equation for the $^3\Sigma_g^-$ state is expressed in terms of the molecular π_g functions denoted π^+ and π^-, according to whether their momenta are directed parallel or antiparallel to the molecular axis. There are two atomic p orbitals per π function, again denoted p^+ or p^- with respect to the molecular axis;

$$\pi^+ = \frac{p_1^+ - p_2^+}{[2(1-S)]^{1/2}}$$

$$\pi^- = \frac{p_1^- - p_2^-}{[2(1-S)]^{1/2}}.$$

In order to evaluate

$$\psi(^3\Sigma_g^-)|\xi\hat{l}\cdot\hat{s}|\psi(^1\Sigma_g^+)$$

we expand equations (43.1) and (43.4) using the above equations and apply the results of Appendix V. Since, in units of $h/(2\pi)$,

$$\hat{M}_z|p^+\rangle = |p^+\rangle$$
$$\hat{M}_z|p^-\rangle = -|p^-\rangle$$
$$\hat{S}_z|\alpha\rangle = \tfrac{1}{2}|\alpha\rangle$$
$$\hat{S}_z|\beta\rangle = -\tfrac{1}{2}|\beta\rangle$$

we derive from the results of Appendix V that

$$\hat{M}_+|p^+\rangle = \hat{M}_-|p^-\rangle = 0$$
$$\hat{M}_+|p^-\rangle = \hat{M}_-|p^+\rangle = \sqrt{2}|p^0\rangle$$
$$\hat{S}_+|\alpha\rangle = \hat{S}_-|\beta\rangle = 0$$
$$\hat{S}_+|\beta\rangle = |\alpha\rangle$$
$$\hat{S}_-|\alpha\rangle = |\beta\rangle.$$

181

Using equation (36.3) it can be found that for p^+,

$$\xi\mathbf{l} \cdot \mathbf{s} = \xi(\hat{M}_z\hat{S}_z + \tfrac{1}{2}\hat{M}_+\hat{S}_- + \tfrac{1}{2}\hat{M}_-\hat{S}_+)|p^+\rangle$$

$$= \tfrac{1}{2}\xi$$

and therefore that $\xi\mathbf{l} \cdot \mathbf{s}$ is $\tfrac{1}{2}\xi$ for π^+ also. Altogether we find

$$\hat{l} \cdot \hat{s}|\pi^+\rangle = \tfrac{1}{2}|\pi^+\rangle$$

$$\hat{l} \cdot \hat{s}|\bar{\pi}^-\rangle = \tfrac{1}{2}|\bar{\pi}^-\rangle$$

$$\hat{l} \cdot \hat{s}|\bar{\pi}^+\rangle = -\tfrac{1}{2}|\bar{\pi}^+\rangle + \frac{1}{\sqrt{2}}|\pi^0\rangle$$

$$\hat{l} \cdot \hat{s}|\pi^-\rangle = -\tfrac{1}{2}|\pi^-\rangle + \frac{1}{\sqrt{2}}|\bar{\pi}^0\rangle$$

and the matrix of the spin–orbit operator for equation (43.1) is as follows.

	$\pi^+\bar{\pi}^-$	$\bar{\pi}^+\pi^-$	$-\pi^-\bar{\pi}^+$	$-\bar{\pi}^-\pi^+$
$\pi^+\bar{\pi}^-$	$+\xi$	0	0	0
$\bar{\pi}^+\pi^-$	0	$-\xi$	0	0
$-\pi^-\bar{\pi}^+$	0	0	$-\xi$	0
$-\bar{\pi}^-\pi^+$	0	0	0	ξ

Cancellation of terms in the above means that for $^3\Sigma_g^-$, $\xi\mathbf{l} \cdot \mathbf{s} = 0$. The same result is obtained using equation (43.4) for $^1\Sigma_g^+$. However, the off-diagonal term $\langle^3\Sigma_g^-|\xi\hat{l} \cdot \hat{s}|^1\Sigma_g^+\rangle$ has the magnitude ξ.

References

Almenningen A, Anderson B and Astrup E E 1970 *Acta Chem. Scand.* **24** 1579

Åsbrink L 1972 *Chem. Phys. Lett.* **15** 56

Åsbrink L, Lindholm E and Edqvist O 1970a *Chem. Phys. Lett.* **7** 549

—— 1970b *Chem. Phys. Lett.* **5** 609

Baerends E J and Ros P 1975 *Molec. Phys.* **30** 1735

Bagus P S, Liu B, Liskow D H and Schaefer H F 1975 *J. Am. Chem. Soc.* **97** 7216

Baker C and Turner D W 1968 *Proc. R. Soc.* **A308** 19

Basch H, Robin M B, Kuebler N A, Baker C and Turner D W 1969 *J. Chem. Phys.* **51** 52

Bastide J and Maier J P 1976 *Chem. Phys.* **12** 177

Beez M, Biere G, Bock H and Heilbronner E 1973 *Helv. Chim. Acta* **56** 1028

Berkowitz J 1975 *J. Chem. Phys.* **62** 4074

Berkowitz J and Spohr R 1973 *J. Electron Spectrosc.* **2** 143

Brogli F and Heilbronner E 1971 *Helv. Chim. Acta* **54** 1423

Brundle C R and Jones G R 1972 *J. Chem. Soc. Faraday Trans. II* **68** 959

Brundle C R, Jones G R and Basch H 1971 *J. Chem. Phys.* **55** 1098

Brundle C R, Kuebler N A, Robin M B and Basch H 1972a *Inorg. Chem.* **11** 20

Brundle C R, Robin M B and Basch H 1970a *J. Chem. Phys.* **53** 2196

Brundle C R, Robin M B, Basch H, Pinsky M and Bond A 1970b *J. Am. Chem. Soc.* **92** 3863

Brundle C R, Robin M B and Jones G R 1970c *J. Chem. Phys.* **52** 3383

Brundle C R, Robin M B, Kuebler N A and Basch H 1972b *J. Am. Chem. Soc.* **94** 1451

Buenker R J and Peyerimhoff S D 1974 *Chem. Rev.* **74** 127

Bulgin D K, Dyke J M and Morris A 1977 *Trans. Faraday Soc.* **73** 2225

Bull W E, Pullen B P, Grimm F A, Moddeman W E, Schweitzer G K and Carlson T A 1970 *Inorg. Chem.* **9** 2474

Burroughs P, Evans S, Hamnett A, Orchard A F and Richardson N V 1974 *J. Chem. Soc. Commun.* 921

Cambray J, Gasteiger J, Steitwieser A and Bagus P S 1974 *J. Am. Chem. Soc.* **96** 5978

Caprace G, Delwiche J, Natalis P and Collin J E 1976 *Chem. Phys.* **13** 43

Carlson T A 1971 *Chem. Phys. Lett* **9** 23

Carlson T A and Anderson C P 1971 *Chem. Phys. Lett.* **10** 561

Carroll T X, Shaw R W, Thomas T D, Kindle C and Bartlett N 1974 *J. Am. Chem. Soc.* **96** 1989

Cetinkaya B, King G H, Krishnamurthy S S, Lappert M F and Pedley J B 1971 *Chem. Commun.* 1370

Condon E U and Shortley G H 1964 *The Theory of Atomic Spectra* (London: Cambridge University Press)

Cornford A B, Frost D C, Herring F G and McDowell C A 1971 *J. Chem. Phys.* **55** 2820

Coulson C A 1964 *J. Chem. Soc.* 1442

Coulson C A, Streitwieser A, Poole M D and Brauman J I 1965 *Dictionary of π-Electron Calculations* (New York: Pergamon)

Cox P A, Evans S, Hamnett A and Orchard A F 1970 *Chem. Phys. Lett.* **7** 414

Cradock S 1971 *Chem. Phys. Lett.* **10** 291

Cradock S, Donovan R J, Duncan W and Gillespie H M 1975 *Trans. Faraday Soc. Dalton II* **71** 156

Cradock S and Duncan W 1974 *Molec. Phys.* **27** 837

Delwiche J, Natali P, Momigny J and Collin J E 1973 *J. Electron Spectrosc.* **1** 219

Demuynk J and Veillard A 1973 *Theor. Chim. Acta* **28** 241

Desclaux J 1972 *Int. J. Quantum. Chem.* **6** 25

Dill D 1973 *Phys. Rev.* **A7** 1976

Dixon R N and Hull S E 1969 *Chem. Phys. Lett.* **3** 367

Edqvist O, Åsbrink L and Lindholm E 1971 *Z. Naturf.* **26A** 1407

El-Sayed M F A, Kasha M and Tanaka Y 1961 *J. Chem. Phys.* **34** 596

Evans S, Green J C and Jackson S E 1972a *J. Chem. Soc. Faraday Trans. II* **68** 249

Evans S, Green J C, Joachim P J, Orchard A F, Maier J P and Turner D W 1972b *J. Chem. Soc. Faraday Trans. II* **68** 905

Evans S, Green J C, Orchard A F, Saito T and Turner D W 1969 *Chem. Phys. Lett.* **4** 361

Evans S and Orchard A F 1971 *Inorg. Chim. Acta* **5** 81

Foster S, Felps S, Cusachs L C and McGlynn S P 1973 *J. Am. Chem. Soc.* **95** 5521

Frost D C, Lee S T and McDowell C A 1973a *J. Chem. Phys.* **59** 5484

—— 1973b *Chem. Phys. Lett.* **23** 472

Gardner J L and Samson J A R 1973 *J. Electron Spectrosc.* **2** 259

—— 1974 *Chem. Phys. Lett.* **26** 240

—— 1976 *J. Electron Spectrosc.* **8** 123

Gelius U and Siegbahn K 1972 *ESCA Studies of Molecular Core and Valence Levels in the Gas Phase, Uppsala University Institute of Physics* UUIP-794

Gilmore F R 1965 *J. Quantum Spectrosc. Radiat. Transfer* **5** 369

Goldstein M J, Leight R S, Lipton M S, Bieri G, Heilbronner E, Kobayashi T and Schmelzer A 1976 *Helv. Chim. Acta* **59** 2657

Green J C, Green M L H, Joachim P J, Orchard A F and Turner D W 1970 *Phil. Trans. R. Soc.* **A268** 111

Hancock W H and Samson J A R 1976 *J. Electron Spectrosc.* **9** 211

Haselbach E 1970 *Chem. Phys. Lett.* **7** 428

Head R A, Nixon J F, Sharp G J and Clark R J 1975 *J. Chem. Soc. Dalton Trans.* 2054

Herman F and Skillman S 1963 *Atomic Structure Calculations* (Englewood Cliffs, NJ: Prentice-Hall)

Herzberg G 1944, 1950, 1966 *Molecular Spectra and Molecular Structure* vols 1–3 (New York: Van Nostrand)

Higginson B R, Lloyd D R, Burroughs P, Gibson D M and Orchard A F 1973 *J. Chem. Soc. Faraday Trans. II* **69** 1659

Hillier I H, Guest M F, Higginson B R and Lloyd D R 1974 *Molec. Phys.* **27** 215

Hillier I H and Kendrick J 1976 *Inorg. Chem.* **15** 520

Hillier I H and Saunders V R 1971 *Molec. Phys.* **22** 1025

Hillier I H, Saunders V R, Ware M J, Bassett P J, Lloyd D R and Lynaugh N 1970 *Chem. Commun.* 1316

Itah J 1977 *Chem. Phys. Lett.* **47** 245

Jolly W F 1972 *Electron Spectroscopy* ed D A Shirley (Amsterdam: North-Holland)

Jonas A E, Schweitzer G K, Grimm F A and Carlson T E 1972 *J. Electron Spectrosc.* **1** 29

Jonathan N, Morris A, Okuda M, Ross K J and Smith D J 1974 *J. Chem. Soc. Faraday Trans. II* **70** 1810

Jorgensen W L and Salem L 1973 *The Organic Chemist's Book of Orbitals* (New York: Academic Press)

Kauzmann W 1957 *Quantum Chemistry* (New York: Academic Press)

Klemperer O 1971 *Electron Optics* (London: Cambridge University Press)

Lazzeretti P and Zanasi R 1976 *Chem. Phys. Lett.* **42** 411

Lee S T, Süzer S and Shirley D A 1976 *Chem. Phys. Lett.* **41** 52

Lee T H and Rabalais J W 1975 *Chem. Phys. Lett.* **34** 135

Lempka H J, Passmore T R and Price W C 1968 *Proc. R. Soc.* **A304** 53

Lindholm E 1972 *Electron Emission Spectroscopy* ed W Dekeyser *et al* (Dordrecht, Holland: Reidel) p 259

Lloyd D R and Lynaugh N 1971 *Chem. Commun.* 627

Longuet-Higgins H C 1961 *Adv. Spectrosc.* **2** 429

Manne R, Wittel K and Mohanty B S 1975 *Molec. Phys.* **29** 485

Manson S T 1973 *J. Electron Spectrosc.* **1** 413

Marr G V 1976 *Photoelectron Emission: Proc. Daresbury Study Weekend* **9** 81 (Daresbury Laboratory, Warrington: Science Research Council)

Marriot J C, Salthouse J A and Ware M J 1970 *Chem. Commun.* 595

Meyer W 1971 *Int. J. Quantum Chem.* **5** 341

Moore C E 1949, 1952, 1958 *Atomic Energy Levels* vols 1–3 *National Bureau of Standards Circular No.* 467

Mott N F and Sneddon I N 1948 *Wave Mechanics and its Applications* (New York: Dover)

Mulliken R S 1949 *J. Chim. Phys.* **46** 675

—— 1976 *Acc. Chem. Res.* **9** 7

Mulliken R S, Rieke C A, Orloff D and Orloff H 1949 *J. Chem. Phys.* **17** 1248

Narayan B and Murrell J N 1970 *Molec. Phys.* **19** 169

von Niessen W, Cederbaum L S, Diercksen G H F and Hohlneicher G 1975 *Chem. Phys.* **11** 399

von Niessen W, Cederbaum L S, Domcke W and Diercksen G H F 1976 *Molec. Phys.* **32** 1057

Orchard A F and Richardson N V 1975 *J. Electron Spectrosc.* **6** 61

Pauling L 1960 *The Nature of the Chemical Bond* (Ithaca, NY: Cornell University Press)

—— 1970 *Chem. Br.* **6** 468

Pauling L and Wilson E B 1935 *Introduction to Quantum Mechanics* (New York: McGraw-Hill)

Peatman W B 1976 *J. Chem. Phys.* **64** 4093

Potts A W, Lempka H J, Streets D G and Price W C 1970 *Phil. Trans. R. Soc.* **A268** 59

Potts A W and Price W C 1971 *Trans. Faraday Soc.* **67** 1242

—— 1972 *Proc. R. Soc.* **A326** 181

Potts A W and Streets D G 1974 *J. Chem. Soc. Faraday Trans. II* **70** 875

Potts A W and Williams T A 1976 *Chem. Phys. Lett.* **42** 550

Rabalais J W, Karlsson L, Werme L O, Bergmark T and Siegbahn K 1972 *Analysis of Vibrational Structure and Jahn–Teller Effects in the Electron Spectrum of Ammonia, Uppsala University Institute of Physics* UUIP-797

Rabalais J W and Katrib A 1974 *Molec. Phys.* **27** 923

Robinson H and Rawlinson W F 1914 *Phil. Mag.* **28** 277

Rohmer M and Veillard A 1973 *Chem. Commun.* 250

Rosén A 1978 *Chem. Phys. Lett.* **55** 311

Samson J A R and Gardner J L 1973 *Phys. Rev. Lett.* **31** 1327

—— 1976 *J. Electron Spectrosc.* **8** 35

Schulman J M and Moskowitz J W 1967 *J. Chem. Phys.* **47** 3491

Schweig A and Thiel W 1974 *J. Chem. Phys.* **60** 951

Siegbahn K 1975 *Electron Spectroscopy and Molecular Structure, Uppsala University Institute of Physics* UUIP-909

Siegbahn K, Nordling C, Fahman A, Nordberg R, Hamrin K, Hedman J, Johansson G, Bergmark T, Karlsom S, Lindgren L and Lindberg B 1967 *ESCA: Atomic Molecular and Solid State Structure Studied by Means of Electron Spectroscopy* (Uppsala: Almqvist and Wiksells)

Siegbahn K, Nordling C, Johansson G, Hedman J, Heden P F, Hamrin K, Gelius U, Bergmark T, Werme L O, Manne R and Baer Y 1969 *ESCA Applied to Free Molecules* (Amsterdam: North-Holland)

Slater J C 1960 *Quantum Theory of Atomic Structure* (New York: McGraw-Hill)

Snyder L C and Basch H 1972 *Molecular Wave Functions and Properties* (New York: Wiley)

Streitwieser A 1962 *Molecular Orbital Theory* (New York: Wiley)

Süzer S, Banna M S and Shirley D A 1975 *J. Chem. Phys.* **63** 3473

Terenin A and Vilessov F 1964 *Adv. Photochem.* **2** 385

Thomas R K and Thompson Sir H 1974 *Proc. R. Soc.* **A339** 29

Topiol S and Ratner M A 1977 *Chem. Phys.* **20** 1

Turner D W, Baker C, Baker A D and Brundle C R 1970 *Molecular Photoelectron Spectroscopy* (New York: Wiley)

Weber J 1977 *Chem. Phys. Lett.* **45** 261

Weisler 1956 *Handb. Phys.* **21** 304 (Berlin: Springer)

Index